CDX Learning Systems

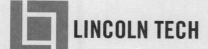
LINCOLN TECH

Lincoln Technical Institute
Tasksheet Manual

VOLUME 1

JONES & BARTLETT
LEARNING

World Headquarters
Jones & Bartlett Learning
5 Wall Street
Burlington, MA 01803
978-443-5000
info@jblearning.com
www.jblearning.com

Jones & Bartlett Learning books and products are available through most bookstores and online booksellers. To contact Jones & Bartlett Learning directly, call 800-832-0034, fax 978-443-8000, or visit our website, www.jblearning.com.

978-1284-16481-7

Production Credits

General Manager: Kimberly Brophy
VP, Product Development: Christine Emerton
Product Manager: Jesse Mitchell
Product Owner: Kevin Murphy
Senior Vendor Manager: Sara Kelly
Marketing Manager: Amanda Banner
Manufacturing and Inventory Control Supervisor: Amy Bacus
Solution Specialist: Douglas Robertson
Composition and Project Management: Integra Software Services Pvt. Ltd.
Cover Design: Scott Moden
Director of Rights & Media: Joanna Gallant
Rights & Media Specialist: Robert Boder
Media Development Editor: Shannon Sheehan
Cover Image (Title Page, L to R): © Umberto Shtanzman/Shutterstock; © Shutterstock/IM_photo
Printing and Binding: McNaughton & Gunn
Cover Printing: McNaughton & Gunn

Library of Congress Cataloging-in-Publication Data

6048

Printed in the United States of America
22 21 20   10 9 8 7 6 5

Contents

Time off_____

Time on_____

Total time_____

CDX Tasksheet Number: C451

1. **List the location(s) of the following items.**

   a. **Program's general shop rules and policies:**

   b. **Safety Data Sheets (SDS) book:**

   c. **Procedure for operation of a fire extinguisher:**

   d. **Procedure for operation of a vehicle hoist:**

2. **List the shop's policy for the wearing of safety glasses while in the shop:**

3. **List the shop's policy for driving vehicles:**

4. **List the shop's policy for clothing in the shop:**

5. **List the shop's policy for jewelry in the shop:**

6. **Pass the shop's safety test and record your score here:** _____

7. **Have your supervisor/instructor verify satisfactory completion of this procedure, any observations found, and any necessary action(s) recommended.**

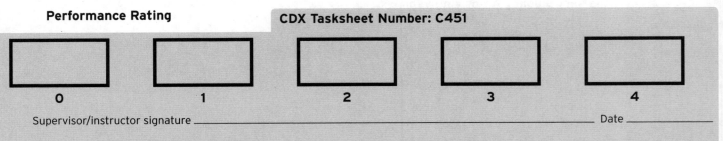

Performance Rating

CDX Tasksheet Number: C451

0	1	2	3	4

Supervisor/instructor signature _____ Date _____

© 2019 Jones & Bartlett Learning, LLC, an Ascend Learning Company

MAST
0A9

Time off_____

Time on_____

Total time_____

CDX Tasksheet Number: C460

1. Research the location and purpose of evacuation routes.

    a. Describe the purpose of evacuation routes:

2. Label the evacuation route(s) on the diagram of the shop at the end of this section. Also label the location of the posted evacuation route diagram(s).

3. Have your supervisor/instructor verify satisfactory completion of this procedure, any observations found, and any necessary action(s) recommended.

© 2019 Jones & Bartlett Learning, LLC, an Ascend Learning Company

Performance Rating

CDX Tasksheet Number: C460

0	1	2	3	4

Supervisor/instructor signature _____ Date _____

MAST
0A6

Time off_____

Time on_____

Total time_____

CDX Tasksheet Number: C456

1. **Research the uniform color code system used to designate safety areas in a shop. List each color and its designation:**

   a. **Color:** _____ **designates:** _____

   b. **Color:** _____ **designates:** _____

   c. **Color:** _____ **designates:** _____

   d. **Color:** _____ **designates:** _____

2. **Label all of the marked safety areas on the diagram of the shop at the end of this section.**

3. **Have your supervisor/instructor verify satisfactory completion of this procedure, any observations found, and any necessary action(s) recommended.**

Performance Rating

CDX Tasksheet Number: C456

0	1	2	3	4

Supervisor/instructor signature _____ Date _____

▶ **TASK** Identify the location and the types of fire extinguishers and other fire safety equipment; demonstrate knowledge of the procedures for using fire extinguishers and other fire safety equipment.

MAST
OA7

Time off_____

Time on_____

Total time_____

CDX Tasksheet Number: C458

1. **Research the types, location, and use of fire extinguishers.**
   a. **List the different types of fire extinguishers (dry chemical, CO_2, etc.) available:**

   i. **Type:** _____ ; **for use on what class of fire:** _____

   ii. **Type:** _____ ; **for use on what class of fire:** _____

   iii. **Type:** _____ ; **for use on what class of fire:** _____

   iv. **Type:** _____ ; **for use on what class of fire:** _____

   In the above list, put a star next to the type(s) of fire extinguishers in this shop.

2. **List the steps for proper use of a fire extinguisher:**

3. **Research the location, purpose, and use of fire blankets in your shop.**
   a. **Describe the purpose of a fire blanket (under what circumstances should a fire blanket be used?):**

   b. **Describe how a fire blanket puts out a fire:**

4. **Label the location of all fire extinguishers on the diagram of the shop at the end of this section.**

5. **Label the location of the fire blanket(s) on the diagram of the shop at the end of this section.**

6. Have your supervisor/instructor verify satisfactory completion of this procedure, any observations found, and any necessary action(s) recommended.

Performance Rating

CDX Tasksheet Number: C458

0	1	2	3	4

Supervisor/instructor signature _____ Date _____

MAST
0A8

CDX Tasksheet Number: C459

1. **Research the location, purpose, and use of eye wash stations in your shop.**

   a. **Describe the purpose of an eye wash station:**

   b. **Describe the proper use of an eye wash station (including time):**

   c. **What type of eye injury would use of an eye wash station NOT be appropriate for?**

2. **Label the location of the eye wash station(s) on the diagram of the shop at the end of this section.**

3. **Have your supervisor/instructor verify satisfactory completion of this procedure, any observations found, and any necessary action(s) recommended.**

Performance Rating

CDX Tasksheet Number: C459

0	1	2	3	4

Supervisor/instructor signature _____ Date _____

▶ **TASK** Locate and demonstrate knowledge of safety data sheets (SDS).

Time off_____

Time on_____

Total time_____

CDX Tasksheet Number: C465

1. **List the safety precautions when handling motor oil:**

2. **List the flash point of gasoline/petroleum:** _____ °F/°C

3. **List the firefighting equipment needed to put out a gasoline/petroleum fire:**

4. **List the first aid treatment for battery acid in the eyes:**

5. **List the first aid treatment for ingestion of antifreeze (ethylene glycol):**

6. **Label the location of the SDS books on the diagram of the shop at the end of this section.**

7. **Have your supervisor/instructor verify satisfactory completion of this procedure, any observations found, and any necessary action(s) recommended.**

Performance Rating

CDX Tasksheet Number: C465

0	1	2	3	4

Supervisor/instructor signature _____ Date _____

▶ TASK Draw a diagram of the shop and label all parts. **Additional Task**

CDX Tasksheet Number: N/A

Time off_____

Time on_____

Total time_____

1. On a full-sized piece of paper, draw a diagram of the shop and label each of the following:

      a. Marked safety areas (floor lines, etc.) _____ (X when finished)
      b. Location of the fire blanket(s) _____ (X when finished)
      c. Location of all fire extinguishers _____ (X when finished)
      d. Location of the exhaust fan switch(es) _____ (X when finished)
      e. Location of the electrical disconnect switch(es) _____ (X when finished)
      f. Location of the eye wash station(s) _____ (X when finished)
      g. Location of the SDS books _____ (X when finished)
      h. Evacuation route(s) _____ (X when finished)
      i. Location of the master air shut-off valve _____ (X when finished)
      j. Location of the over-head door switch(es) _____ (X when finished)

2. Have your supervisor/instructor verify satisfactory completion of this task.

Performance Rating　　　　　　　　　　　CDX Tasksheet Number: N/A

0	1	2	3	4

Supervisor/instructor signature _____ Date _____

Comply with the required use of safety glasses, ear protection, gloves, and shoes during lab/shop activities.

MAST
OA10

Time off_____

Time on_____

Total time_____

CDX Tasksheet Number: C461

1. Describe the safety glasses policy for your shop (be specific):

2. Describe the policy related to ear protection in the shop (be specific):

3. Describe the policy related to gloves for your shop (be specific):

4. Describe the policy related to work shoes for your shop (be specific):

5. These tasks require observation of the student over a prolonged period. Ask your instructor to give you a date for your evaluation.

   a. Write that date here: _____

6. Continue with your projects, complying with the safe use of safety glasses, gloves, shoes, clothing, and hair containment during all lab/shop activities.

7. On or after that date, have your instructor verify satisfactory completion of these tasks.

Performance Rating

CDX Tasksheet Number: C461

0	1	2	3	4

Supervisor/instructor signature _____ Date _____

MAST
OA11

Time off_____

Time on_____

Total time_____

CDX Tasksheet Number: C462

1. Describe the clothing requirements for your shop (be specific):

2. These tasks require observation of the student over a prolonged period. Ask your instructor to give you a date for your evaluation.

   a. Write that date here: _____

3. Continue with your projects, complying with the safe use of safety glasses, gloves, shoes, clothing, and hair containment during all lab/shop activities.

4. On or after that date, have your instructor verify satisfactory completion of these tasks.

© 2019 Jones & Bartlett Learning, LLC, an Ascend Learning Company

Performance Rating

CDX Tasksheet Number: C462

0	1	2	3	4

Supervisor/instructor signature _____ Date _____

MAST
OA12

CDX Tasksheet Number: C463

1. List your shop's policy concerning securing hair in the shop (be specific):

2. List your shop's policy concerning jewelry in the shop (be specific):

3. These tasks require observation of the student over a prolonged period. Ask your instructor to give you a date for your evaluation.

   a. Write that date here: _____

4. Continue with your projects, complying with the safe use of safety glasses, gloves, shoes, clothing, and hair containment during all lab/shop activities.

5. On or after that date, have your instructor verify satisfactory completion of these tasks.

Performance Rating

CDX Tasksheet Number: C463

0	1	2	3	4

Supervisor/instructor signature _____ Date _____

► **TASK** Utilize proper ventilation procedures for working within the lab/shop area.

MAST
OA5

Time off_____

Time on_____

Total time_____

CDX Tasksheet Number: C455

1. **List the OSHA personal exposure limit for carbon monoxide over an 8-hour work period:** _____ **ppm**

2. **Properly position a vehicle in a work stall.**

3. **Properly connect the exhaust extraction system to the vehicle exhaust.**

4. **Turn on, or verify that the extraction system is on.**

5. **With your instructor's permission, start the vehicle and verify the extraction equipment is secure and operating properly.**

6. **Have your instructor verify your previously given answer, and proper exhaust extraction usage. Supervisor/instructor's initials:** _____

7. **Turn off the vehicle, return the exhaust hoses to their proper storage places, and shut off the extraction system if it isn't being used anymore.**

8. **Have your supervisor/instructor verify satisfactory completion of this procedure, any observations found, and any necessary action(s) recommended.**

Performance Rating

CDX Tasksheet Number: C455

0	1	2	3	4

Supervisor/instructor signature _____ Date _____

Proper vehicle identification information: Define the use and purpose of the VIN, engine numbers, and data code; locate the VIN, and apply knowledge of VIN information.

Time off_____

Time on_____

Total time_____

CDX Tasksheet Number: N/A

1. **Research the location and description of the VIN in an appropriate service manual.**

    a. **Location of VIN:** _____

    b. **VIN:**_____

2. **Using the VIN on the vehicle assigned to you, identify the following information. (Write both corresponding VIN code designation and what it represents.)**

    a. **Country of origin:** _____

    b. **Location of manufacturing plant:** _____

    c. **Passenger restraint system:** _____

    d. **Engine designation:** _____

    e. **Model year:**_____

3. **Which position in the VIN is the model year?** _____

4. **Which position in the VIN is the engine designation?** _____

5. **Have your supervisor/instructor verify satisfactory completion of this procedure, any observations found, and any necessary action(s) recommended.**

Performance Rating

CDX Tasksheet Number: N/A

0	1	2	3	4

Supervisor/instructor signature _____ Date _____

► **TASK** Identify information needed and the service
requested on a repair order.

MAST
OC1

Time off_____

Time on_____

Total time_____

CDX Tasksheet Number: C472

1. **Familiarize yourself with the assigned repair order. Locate and list the following information below.**

   a. **Date:** _____
   b. **Customer:** _____
   c. **Address:** _____
   d. **Daytime phone number:** _____
   e. **Year:** _____
   f. **Make:** _____
   g. **Model:** _____
   h. **Color:** _____
   i. **License and state:** _____
   j. **Odometer reading:** _____
   k. **VIN:** _____
   l. **Customer concern(s)/service requested:**

2. **Did the customer sign the repair order authorizing the repairs?**
   Yes: _____ **No:** _____

3. **Return the sample repair order to its proper storage place.**

4. **Have your supervisor/instructor verify satisfactory completion of this procedure, any observations found, and any necessary action(s) recommended.**

Performance Rating

CDX Tasksheet Number: C472

0	1	2	3	4

Supervisor/instructor signature _____ Date _____

MAST
OC5

Time off_____

Time on_____

Total time_____

CDX Tasksheet Number: C590

Vehicle used for this activity:

Year _____ Make _____ Model _____

Odometer _____ VIN _____

1. **Use your company's repair order to complete this task.**

   Fred Smith brings in a 2008 Hyundai Santa Fe AWD, with a 3.3 L engine, automatic transmission, 72,426 miles on the odometer, silver paint, VIN 5NMSH73E28H192794. It needs some work before going on a 3000-mile trip. He would like an estimate of repairs needed and has agreed to let your technician inspect the vehicle while you write up the repair order. He gives you the following information:

   a. **Home address: 1234 NE Main Street, Anytown, CA 13579**
   b. **Cell phone: (111) 222-1234**
   c. **Work phone: (111) 333-4567**
   d. **Vehicle license number: CDX - 111**

2. **The customer listed the following concern/complaints:**

   a. **Small oil leak from under the engine**
   b. **Small coolant leak from under the engine**
   c. **Squealing noise coming from the front brakes**

3. **The technician found the following conditions:**

   a. **Both valve covers have leaking gaskets.**
   b. **The water pump is leaking from the shaft and the bearing is worn.**
   c. **The front brake pads are worn down to the wear indicators, the rotors are a bit under specifications, and the calipers are starting to seep brake fluid past the caliper piston seal and need to be replaced.**

4. **Complete the repair order as if all tasks were completed including parts, their cost, and labor.**

5. **Have your supervisor/instructor verify satisfactory completion of this procedure, any observations found, and any necessary action(s) recommended.**

Performance Rating

CDX Tasksheet Number: C590

0	1	2	3	4

Supervisor/instructor signature _____ Date _____

MAST
OC4

Time off_____

Time on_____

Total time_____

CDX Tasksheet Number: C475

1. Familiarize yourself with the repair history as listed on the repair orders and answer the following questions.

    a. What was the first date this vehicle was serviced? _____

    b. What was the last date this vehicle was serviced? _____

    c. What was the most major repair performed?

    d. Was this vehicle ever returned for the same problem more than once? Yes: _____ No: _____

       i. If so, for what and how many times? _____

    e. Compare this list to the scheduled maintenance chart and list any missed maintenance tasks between the first service and the last service:

2. Have your supervisor/instructor verify satisfactory completion of this procedure, any observations found, and any necessary action(s) recommended.

Performance Rating

CDX Tasksheet Number: C475

0	1	2	3	4

Supervisor/instructor signature _____ Date _____

▶ **TASK** Demonstrate use of the three Cs (concern, cause, and correction).

MAST
OC3

Time off_____

Time on_____

Total time_____

CDX Tasksheet Number: C474

1. **Using the following scenario, write up the three Cs as listed on most repair orders. Assume that the customer authorized the recommended repairs.**

   A customer complains that his vehicle is leaving what looks like oil spots on the landlord's driveway after he ran over something in the road a few days ago. You check the engine oil find that it is about 1/2 a quart low, but looks pretty clean, like it was changed recently. The engine oil life monitor indicates 92% oil life remaining. You safely raise and secure the vehicle on the hoist. While visually inspecting the underside of the vehicle, you notice oil dripping off of the engine oil drain plug. Checking the torque of the drain plug shows that the drain plug isn't loose. Closer inspection reveals a shiny spot on the aluminum oil pan near the drain plug. There is a small crack in the oil pan that is seeping oil and dripping slowly off of the drain plug.

2. **Concern/complaint:**

3. **Cause:**

4. **Correction:**

5. **Have your supervisor/instructor verify satisfactory completion of the previous answers, and any necessary action(s) recommended.**

Performance Rating

CDX Tasksheet Number: C474

0	1	2	3	4

Supervisor/instructor signature _____ Date _____

▶ **TASK** Demonstrate safe handling and use of appropriate tools.

MAST
OB3

Time off_____

Time on_____

Total time_____

CDX Tasksheet Number: C468

1. These tasks will require observation of the student over a prolonged period after the initial check. Ask your instructor to give you a date for your evaluation.

   a. Write that date here: _____

2. Continue with your other projects, demonstrating safe handling, proper cleaning, maintenance, and storage of the tools until the date of your evaluation.

3. On or after that date, have your instructor verify satisfactory completion of each task.

Performance Rating

CDX Tasksheet Number: C468

0	1	2	3	4

Supervisor/instructor signature _____ Date _____

► **TASK** Utilize safe procedures for handling of tools and equipment.

MAST
0A2

Time off_____

Time on_____

Total time_____

CDX Tasksheet Number: C452

1. These tasks will require observation of the student over a prolonged period after the initial check. Ask your instructor to give you a date for your evaluation.

   a. Write that date here: _____

2. Continue with your other projects, utilizing safe handling of tools and equipment including proper cleaning, maintenance, and storage of the tools and equipment until the date of your evaluation.

3. On or after that date, have your instructor verify satisfactory completion of each task.

Performance Rating

CDX Tasksheet Number: C452

0	1	2	3	4

Supervisor/instructor signature _____ Date _____

Time off_____

Time on_____

Total time_____

CDX Tasksheet Number: C467

1. **Complete the following conversions from metric to standard and vice versa using the conversion charts below.**

Volume

Volume is the amount of space occupied by a three-dimensional object. The metric system uses liters (l) or cubic centimeters (cc or cm^3). The Imperial system uses gallons (gal) and quarts (qt) for "wet" volume and cubic feet (ft^3) for "dry" volume. You'll need to determine volume any time you fill a vehicle's reservoir with liquid. This includes petrol/gasoline, coolant, oil, transmission fluid, or lubricant.

Volume Conversions	
Imperial-Imperial	4 US qt = 1 US gal 1 ft^3 = 7.48 US gal 1 ft^3 = 6.22 UK gal
Metric-Metric	1 L = 1000 cc 1 cc = 0.001 L
Imperial-Metric	1 $in.^3$ = 16.387 cc 1 US gal = 3.78 L 1 UK gal = 4.54 L 1 US qt = 0.95 L
Metric-Imperial	1 L = 61.0237 $in.^3$ 1 L = 0.035 ft^3 1 L = 0.26 US gal 1 L = 0.21 UK gal 1 L = 1.05 qt

2. **Knowledge Check: Convert the following:**
   a. **3.0 L =** _____ **$in.^3$**
   b. **350 $in.^3$ =** _____ **L**
   c. **3.0 gal =** _____ **L**
   d. **9 L =** _____ **gal**

Mass

Mass is a unit or system of units by which a degree of heaviness is measured. The metric system uses grams (g), kilograms (kg), and tonnes (t). The Imperial system uses ounces (oz), pounds (lb), and tons (T). In the workshop, you will use these measurements to determine the lifting capacity of equipment like hydraulic and engine hoists and floor jacks.

Mass Conversions	
Imperial-Imperial	16 oz = 1 lb 2000 lb = 1 T
Metric-Metric	1000 g = 1 kg 1000 kg = 1 t
Imperial-Metric	1 oz = 28.3 g 1 lb = 453 g 2.2 lb = 1 kg 1 T = 0.907 t
Metric-Imperial	1 t = 1.10 T

3. **Knowledge Check: Convert the following:**
   a. 8 oz = _____ g
   b. 475 g = _____ oz
   c. 6.6 lb = _____ kg
   d. 4500 kg = _____ lb

Torque

Torque is the twisting force applied to a shaft. The metric system uses the Newton meter (Nm). The Imperial system uses the inch-pound (in-lb) and the foot-pound (ft-lb). Vehicle manufacturers specify torque settings for key fasteners on the engine and wheels. You will need to follow the specifications or you could strip threads or break bolts. Torque is also an important concept when discussing engine performance. A foot-pound (ft-lb) is the twisting force applied to a shaft by a lever 1 foot long with a 1-pound mass on the end. A Newton meter (Nm) is the twisting force applied to a shaft by a level 1 meter long with a force of 1 Newton applied to the end of the lever. (1N is equivalent to the force applied by a mass of 100.)

Torque Conversions	
Imperial-Imperial	12 in-lb = 1 ft-lb 1 in-lb = 0.08 ft-lb
Imperial-Metric	1 ft-lb = 1.34 N·m
Metric-Imperial	1 N·m = 0.74 ft-lb 1 N·m = 8.8 in-lb

4. **Knowledge Check: Convert the following:**
   a. 48 in-lb = _____ ft-lb
   b. 15 ft-lb = _____ in-lb
   c. 65 ft-lb = _____ N·m
   d. 142 N·m = _____ ft-lb

Pressure

Pressure is a measurement of force per unit area. The metric system uses kilopascals (kPa) and bar. The Imperial system uses pounds per square inch (psi) and atmospheres. *Vacuum* is a term given to a pressure that is less than atmospheric pressure. The Imperial system measures vacuum in inches of mercury (" Hg) or inches of water. The metric system measures vacuum in millimeters of mercury (mm Hg). You'll need to understand pressure conversions when filling tires and replacing air conditioning refrigerants or using a vacuum gauge.

Pressure Conversions	
Imperial-Imperial	14.7 psi = 1 atmosphere 1" Hg = 14" H_2O 0" Hg = 1 atmosphere
Metric-Metric	100 kPa = 1 bar
Imperial-Metric	1 psi = 6.89 kPa 1 atmosphere = 101.3 kPa 1" Hg = 25.4 mm Hg 1 atmosphere = 1.013 bar

5. **Knowledge Check: Convert the following:**
   a. 14.7 psi = _____ kPa
   b. 650 kPa = _____ psi
   c. 22 psi = _____ bar
   d. 5.5 bar = _____ psi

6. Have your supervisor/instructor verify satisfactory completion of this procedure, any observations found, and any necessary action(s) recommended.

Performance Rating

CDX Tasksheet Number: C467

0	1	2	3	4

Supervisor/instructor signature _____ Date _____

CDX Tasksheet Number: C466

Time off_____

Time on_____

Total time_____

1. **Using the following list, describe the specific function/purpose of each of the following tools and any disadvantages/problems with using the tool, if any:**

    a. **Open-end wrench:**

    b. **Box-end wrench:**

    c. **Socket:**

    d. **Ratchet:**

    e. **Torque wrench:**

    f. **Slotted screwdriver:**

    g. **Phillips screwdriver:**

h. Tap:

i. Die:

j. Feeler blade:

k. Line wrench/flare-nut wrench:

l. Allen wrench:

m. Torx screwdriver or socket:

n. Hacksaw:

o. Oil filter wrench:

© 2019 Jones & Bartlett Learning, LLC, an Ascend Learning Company

p. Compression gauge:

q. DVOM/DMM:

r. Test light:

s. Diagonal side cutters:

t. Locking pliers:

u. Needle-nose pliers:

v. Brake spoon:

w. Micrometer:

x. Dial indicator:

y. Antifreeze hydrometer:

z. Snap-ring pliers:

3. Have your supervisor/instructor verify satisfactory completion of this procedure, any observations found, and any necessary action(s) recommended.

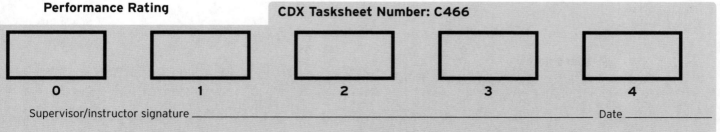

Performance Rating

CDX Tasksheet Number: C466

| 0 | 1 | 2 | 3 | 4 |

Supervisor/instructor signature _____ Date _____

► **TASK** Demonstrate proper use of precision measuring tools
(e.g., micrometer, dial-indicator, dial-caliper).

MAST
OB5

Time off_____

Time on_____

Total time_____

CDX Tasksheet Number: C896

1. **These tasks will require observation of the student over a prolonged period after the initial check. Ask your instructor to give you a date for your evaluation.**

   a. **Write that date here:** _____

2. **Continue with your other projects, demonstrating safe handling, proper cleaning, maintenance, and storage of the tools until the date of your evaluation.**

3. **On or after that date, have your instructor verify satisfactory completion of each task.**

Performance Rating

CDX Tasksheet Number: C896

0	1	2	3	4

Supervisor/instructor signature _____ Date _____

▶ **TASK** Demonstrate proper cleaning, storage, and
maintenance of tools and equipment.

MAST
0B4

Time off_____

Time on_____

Total time_____

CDX Tasksheet Number: C469

1. These tasks will require observation of the student over a prolonged period after the initial check. Ask your instructor to give you a date for your evaluation.

   a. Write that date here: _____

2. Continue with your other projects, demonstrating safe handling, proper cleaning, maintenance, and storage of the tools until the date of your evaluation.

3. On or after that date, have your instructor verify satisfactory completion of each task.

Performance Rating

CDX Tasksheet Number: C469

0	1	2	3	4

Supervisor/instructor signature _____ Date _____

MAST 6B5

Time off_____

Time on_____

Total time_____

CDX Tasksheet Number: C819

> **NOTE** Recharging a battery differs from manufacturer to manufacturer. It is important that you follow the recharging steps recommended by the manufacturer of the battery that is assigned to you.

1. **Research slow and/or fast battery charging for this vehicle battery in the appropriate service information. Follow all directions. If no directions are given, use the following information:**

   It is best to disconnect the negative battery terminal when charging a battery. Consider using a memory minder to maintain the memories on electronic control modules.

   The ideal rate for charging a battery can be found by dividing the battery's CCA by 70.

   To find the maximum charging rate for fast charging a battery, divide the battery's CCA by 40.

   The faster a battery is charged, the shorter its life.

   Do not exceed: 15.5V on a flooded cell battery; 14.8V on an AGM battery; or 14.3V on a gel cell battery.

2. **List the steps for recharging this battery:**

3. **What method is recommended for recharging the battery?**
   Slow charge: _____ **Fast charge:** _____

   a. **Have your supervisor/instructor verify the steps above. Supervisor's/instructor's initials:** _____

4. **Charge the battery according to the manufacturer's recommendations.**

   a. **How long did the battery charge?** _____ **time**
   b. **What was the highest amperage reading during charging?** _____ **amps**
   c. **What was the lowest amperage reading during charging?** _____ **amps**
   d. **What was the highest voltage during charging?** _____ **volts**
   e. **How did you determine the battery was fully charged?**

5. **Determine any necessary action(s):**

6. Have your supervisor/instructor verify satisfactory completion of this procedure, any observations found, and any necessary action(s) recommended.

Performance Rating

CDX Tasksheet Number: C819

0	1	2	3	4

Supervisor/instructor signature _____ Date _____

Jump-start vehicle using jumper cables and a booster battery or an auxiliary power supply.

MAST
6B6

Time off_____

Time on_____

Total time_____

CDX Tasksheet Number: C820

1. Research "starting a vehicle with a dead battery" or "jump starting procedures" in the appropriate service information for the vehicle you are working on. List the steps as outlined in the service information.

> **NOTE** Caution: Some vehicle manufacturers prohibit jump-starting of their vehicles. If this is the case, inform your supervisor/instructor.

> **NOTE** Follow these steps exactly!

2. **Why is the last connection away from the battery, preferably on an unpainted solid metal component connected to the engine block?**

3. **Have your supervisor/instructor verify your answers. Supervisor's/instructor's initials:** _____

4. **Connect the jumper cables as outlined in the service information or connect the auxiliary power supply (jump box) as was outlined in the service information.**

5. **Start the engine.**

6. **Remove the cables in the reverse order as they were installed.**

7. **Have your supervisor/instructor verify satisfactory completion of this procedure, any observations found, and any necessary action(s) recommended.**

© 2019 Jones & Bartlett Learning, LLC, an Ascend Learning Company

Performance Rating

CDX Tasksheet Number: C820

0	1	2	3	4

Supervisor/instructor signature _____ Date _____

▶ **TASK** Perform common fastener and thread repair, to include: remove broken bolt, restore internal and external threads, and repair internal threads with thread insert.

MAST
1A7

CDX Tasksheet Number: C886

> **NOTE** Your instructor may prefer that you perform this task on a mock-up or piece of scrap metal. Ask your instructor how he or she would like you to proceed.

1. **Identify the damaged fastener and its location, and list the information here:**

2. **Research the appropriate method of extracting the broken fastener, and list it here:**

3. **Using the appropriate method, remove the broken bolt from its location. List your observation(s):**

4. **Restore internal and external threads as required, and list your results:**

5. **Have your supervisor/instructor check your work. Supervisor's/instructor's initials:** _____

6. **Repair internal threads with a thread insert using the recommended method. List the steps below:**

7. Have your supervisor/instructor verify satisfactory completion of this procedure, any observations found, and any necessary action(s) recommended.

Performance Rating

CDX Tasksheet Number: C886

0	1	2	3	4

Supervisor/instructor signature _____ Date _____

▶ TASK Identify purpose and demonstrate proper use of fender covers, mats.

Time off_____

Time on_____

Total time_____

CDX Tasksheet Number: C473

1. **Identify the purpose of the following items:**

    a. **Fender cover:**

    b. **Seat cover:**

    c. **Steering wheel cover:**

    d. **Carpet cover/floor mat:**

2. **Properly prepare a vehicle for service or repair, using the above covers.**

3. **Have your supervisor/instructor verify satisfactory completion of this procedure, any observations found, and any necessary action(s) recommended.**

Performance Rating

CDX Tasksheet Number: C473

0	1	2	3	4

Supervisor/instructor signature _____ Date _____

Identify and use proper placement of floor jacks and jack stands.

CDX Tasksheet Number: C453

Time off_____

Time on_____

Total time_____

1. **Research the jacking and lifting procedures for this vehicle in the appropriate service manual.**

    a. **Draw a diagram of the vehicle's lift points:**

2. **Check to make sure the vehicle is on a hard, level surface. If not, move it to a safe location.**

3. **Install wheel chocks. Prepare the floor jack and stands for use.**

4. **Lift and support one end of the vehicle on jack stands according to the manufacturer's procedure.**

    a. **Have your instructor initial to verify proper jack stand placement:**

    _____

5. **Lift the vehicle and remove the jack stands. Return the jack and stands to their proper storage places.**

6. **Return the vehicle to its beginning condition and return any tools you used to their proper locations.**

7. **Have your supervisor/instructor verify satisfactory completion of this procedure, any observations found, and any necessary action(s) recommended.**

Performance Rating

CDX Tasksheet Number: C453

0	1	2	3	4

Supervisor/instructor signature _____ Date _____

► **TASK** Identify and use proper procedures for safe lift operation.

MAST
OA4

Time off_____

Time on_____

Total time_____

CDX Tasksheet Number: C454

Vehicle, if different than above:

Year _____ Make _____ Model_____

Odometer_____ VIN_____

1. **Position the vehicle in proper relation to the lift, taking into consideration the center of gravity of the vehicle.**

   > **NOTE** Check the vehicle for unusual loading, such as heavy loads in the trunk or truck bed. If you find this situation, notify your instructor immediately.

2. **Position the lift arms in the proper location as specified by the manufacturer.**

3. **Raise the lift until one of the arms lightly contacts the lift point. Check the position of the lift arms to make sure they are in contact with (or just about to contact) the proper points.**

   > **NOTE** Make sure the lift arms are not touching or pinching anything they shouldn't be in contact with, including the rocker panel, running boards, and fuel or brake lines, etc.

4. **If the arms are in the proper position, raise the vehicle a few inches off the ground. Using a strong part of the vehicle, moderately shake the vehicle to make sure it is stable.**

   > **NOTE** If the vehicle shifts position at all or is out of balance, lower the vehicle and reset the lift arms or reposition the vehicle.

5. **If the vehicle is stable, lift the vehicle to the height indicated by your instructor and engage the locks or lower the lift onto the locks. Instructor/Supervisor Initial _____**

6. **Verify that there are no obstacles under the vehicle, and that all doors are closed. Lower the vehicle and move the lift arms out of the way of the vehicle.**

7. **Return the vehicle to its beginning condition and return any tools you used to their proper locations.**

© 2019 Jones & Bartlett Learning, LLC, an Ascend Learning Company

8. Have your supervisor/instructor verify satisfactory completion of this procedure, any observations found, and any necessary action(s) recommended.

Performance Rating

CDX Tasksheet Number: C454

0	1	2	3	4

Supervisor/instructor signature _____ Date _____

MAST
OD1

Time off_____

Time on_____

Total time_____

CDX Tasksheet Number: C476

> **NOTE** A properly protected vehicle and good work habits will make this task much easier.

1. **Double check that all work has been completed. Nothing can be missing, loose, or leaking.**

   a. Student initial when completed: _____

2. **If your instructor deems it necessary, test-drive the vehicle to be sure of proper repair and operation of the vehicle.**

   a. Have your instructor initial here: _____

3. **Double check that all tools are put away and stored properly.**

   a. Student initial when completed: _____

4. **Remove all fender covers, seat covers, floor covers, and steering wheel covers. Return them to their storage place or dispose of them properly, depending on the type of cover.**

   a. Student initial when completed: _____

5. **Check the exterior of the vehicle for greasy fingerprints or grime. Clean with an appropriate cleaner. Follow your shop's policies on this procedure.**

   a. Student initial when completed: _____

6. **Check the following interior locations for dirt or greasy spots. Clean with an appropriate cleaner. Follow your shop's policies on this procedure:**

   a. Carpet and floor mats. Student initial when completed: _____
   b. Seats. Student initial when completed: _____
   c. Steering wheel and parking brake handle. Student initial when completed: _____
   d. Door panel and handles. Student initial when completed: _____

7. **If the vehicle is ready to return to the customer, the vehicle may need to be moved out of the shop. Get your instructor's permission to move the vehicle to the customer pick-up area.**

   a. Have your instructor initial here: _____

8. **Return to your work stall and clean up the floor, benches, and related area.**

   a. Student initial when completed: _____

9. Have your supervisor/instructor verify satisfactory completion of this procedure, any observations found, and any necessary action(s) recommended.

Performance Rating

CDX Tasksheet Number: C476

0	1	2	3	4

Supervisor/instructor signature _____ Date _____

► **TASK** Perform engine oil and filter change; use proper fluid type per manufacturer specification.

MAST
1D10

CDX Tasksheet Number: C737

1. **Research the following specifications/procedures for this vehicle in the appropriate service information.**

    a. **Oil capacity:** _____ qt/lt
    b. **Oil viscosity:** _____
    c. **API or other specified rating:** _____
    d. **Oil pan drain plug torque:** _____ ft-lb/N·m
    e. **Oil filter part number:** _____
    f. **List any special requirements/procedures for changing the oil and filter on this vehicle:**

> **NOTE** Some vehicles have more than one oil drain plug and/or a special procedure for changing the filter.

    g. **Determine that a new filter, and the proper oil, is available for this vehicle before proceeding. Yes: _____ No: _____**

2. **Safely raise and secure the vehicle on a hoist.**

> **NOTE** Removing the oil filler cap may allow the oil to drain faster.

3. **Follow the specified procedure for draining the used oil and removing the old oil filter.**

> **NOTE** The oil may be extremely hot. Be sure not to come into contact with the used oil.

    a. **Is the drain plug gasket reusable? Yes: _____ No: _____**
    b. **Did the oil filter gasket come off with the oil filter? Yes: _____ No: _____**
    c. **Have your instructor verify these answers by initialing here: _____**

4. **Once the used oil has been drained, follow the manufacturer's procedure for installing the new oil filter (oil the gasket) and reinstalling the drain plug (tighten to the specified torque).**

5. **Lower the vehicle.**

6. **Following the appropriate service information, add the proper amount of new oil.**

7. Prepare to start the vehicle by applying the parking brake and placing exhaust hoses over the exhaust pipe(s). Start the vehicle and check for oil leaks. If oil leaks are found, shut off the engine immediately, locate the source of the leak, and inform your instructor. If no leaks are found, shut off the engine after a minute or two of running.

8. Let the engine oil drain back into the oil pan for a few minutes and then check to see that the oil is at the proper level. Add oil if necessary.

   a. What is the final oil level? _____

9. Dispose of the old oil and filter according to legislative guidelines (national, federal, state, and local).

10. Reset the maintenance reminder system if equipped, or fill out an oil-change reminder sticker and place it on the vehicle according to your shop's policy.

11. Have your supervisor/instructor verify satisfactory completion of this procedure, any observations found, and any necessary action(s) recommended.

Performance Rating

CDX Tasksheet Number: C737

0	1	2	3	4

Supervisor/instructor signature _____ Date _____

© 2019 Jones & Bartlett Learning, LLC, an Ascend Learning Company

▶ **TASK** Select, handle, store, and fill brake fluids to proper level;
use proper fluid type per manufacturer specification.

MAST
5B9

Time off_____

Time on_____

Total time_____

CDX Tasksheet Number: C239

1. Research the specified brake fluid and the bleeding/flushing procedure for this vehicle using the appropriate service information.

    a. **Specified fluid:**_____

    b. **Bleeding/flushing sequence:**_____

    c. **Bleeding/flushing precautions:**

2. **Locate the master cylinder reservoir.**

    a. **List the level of the brake fluid:**_____

> **NOTE** If the brake fluid is below the minimum level, it could mean there is a leak in the system or the disc brake pads are worn. Investigate these possibilities and report them to your supervisor/instructor.

3. **If appropriate, add the appropriate type of brake fluid to the master cylinder reservoir to bring it to the full mark.**

4. **Knowledge Check: What precautions should be taken when brake fluid is stored?**

5. **Knowledge Check: List the different types of brake fluid available:**

6. **Have your supervisor/instructor verify satisfactory completion of this procedure, any observations found, and any necessary action(s) recommended.**

Performance Rating

CDX Tasksheet Number: C239

0	1	2	3	4

Supervisor/instructor signature _____ Date _____

▶ TASK Inspect proper power steering fluid level and condition.

MAST
4B9

Time off_____

Time on_____

Total time_____

CDX Tasksheet Number: C177

1. **Research specified power steering fluid for this vehicle using the appropriate service information.**

    a. **Specified fluid:** _____

    b. **When should the fluid be checked? Hot:** _____ **Cold:** _____
       Either: _____

    c. **If the service information lists a procedure for flushing the power steering fluid, list the main steps (you can paraphrase, or print off the procedure):**

2. **Follow the manufacturer's procedure to check the fluid level.**

> **NOTE** If power steering fluid is below the minimum level, it could mean there is a leak in the system. Investigate this possibility and report it to your supervisor/instructor.

3. **Locate the power steering-fluid reservoir.**

    a. **List the level of the power steering fluid:** _____

4. **Place a small amount of the fluid from the reservoir on a white piece of paper and describe its condition:**

5. **Determine any necessary action(s):**

6. **Have your supervisor/instructor verify satisfactory completion of this procedure, any observations found, and any necessary action(s) recommended.**

Performance Rating

CDX Tasksheet Number: C177

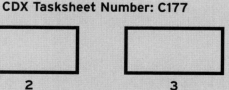

| 0 | 1 | 2 | 3 | 4 |

Supervisor/instructor signature _____ Date _____

▶ TASK Check fluid level in a transmission or a transaxle
equipped with a dipstick.

MAST
2A4

Time off_____

Time on_____

Total time_____

CDX Tasksheet Number: C902

1. **Research the procedure to check the transmission fluid level in the appropriate service information. List the specified steps:**

2. **Following the specified steps, check the transmission fluid level. List level:**

3. **Have your supervisor/instructor verify satisfactory completion of this procedure, any observations found, and any necessary action(s) recommended.**

Performance Rating

CDX Tasksheet Number: C902

0	1	2	3	4

Supervisor/instructor signature _____ Date _____

Inspect, replace, and/or adjust drive belts, tensioners, and pulleys; check pulley and belt alignment.

MAST
1D3

Time off_____

Time on_____

Total time_____

CDX Tasksheet Number: C734

1. Locate "inspecting, adjusting and or replacing a generator (alternator) drive belts, pulleys, and tensioners; check pulley and belt alignment" in the appropriate service information for the vehicle you are working on.

   a. List the specified drive belt tension: _____

   b. List the faults to look for when inspecting drive belts, pulleys, and tensioners:

   c. Describe how to check the correct pulley and belt alignment:

   d. Locate the belt routing diagram, or draw a picture of the current routing arrangement:

2. Remove the vehicle drive belt(s).

3. Inspect the vehicle drive belts, pulleys, and tensioners for faults. List your observations for the following parts:

   a. Vehicle drive belt(s):

b. Pulleys:

c. Tensioner(s):

d. Pulley/belt alignment:

4. **Have your instructor verify the removal of the belt(s) and the faults found. Supervisor's/instructor's initials:** _____

5. **Reinstall the vehicle drive belts using the appropriate service information.**

6. **Re-tension the drive belt(s) using the appropriate service information.**

7. **Check for the correct pulley, tensioner, and drive belt alignment.**

8. **Determine any necessary action(s):**

9. **Have your supervisor/instructor verify satisfactory completion of this procedure, any observations found, and any necessary action(s) recommended.**

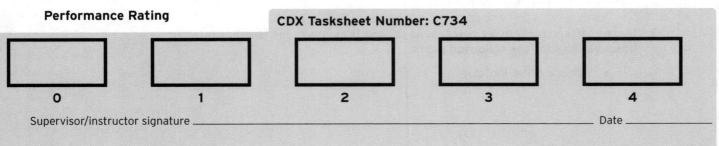

Performance Rating

CDX Tasksheet Number: C734

0	1	2	3	4

Supervisor/instructor signature _____ Date _____

© 2019 Jones & Bartlett Learning, LLC, an Ascend Learning Company

▶ **TASK** Inspect, service, or replace air filters, filter housings, and intake duct work.

MAST 8C5

Time off_____

Time on_____

Total time_____

CDX Tasksheet Number: C962

1. **Research the procedure and specifications for servicing the air filter, housing, and ductwork in the appropriate service information.**

    a. **Specified air filter number:** _____

2. **Following the specified procedure, remove the air filter from the filter housing.**

3. **Inspect the air filter and list the condition:**

4. **Inspect the filter housing and ductwork. List your observations:**

5. **Clean the filter housing following the specified procedure.**

6. **Have your supervisor/instructor verify removal. Supervisor's/instructor's initials:** _____

7. **Following the specified procedure, reinstall the air filter, housing, and ductwork.**

8. **Have your supervisor/instructor verify satisfactory completion of this procedure, any observations found, and any necessary action(s) recommended.**

Performance Rating

CDX Tasksheet Number: C962

0	1	2	3	4

Supervisor/instructor signature _____ Date _____

Verify operation of the instrument panel engine warning indicators.

MAST
1A3

Time off_____

Time on_____

Total time_____

CDX Tasksheet Number: C898

1. **Research the operation of instrument panel gauges/indicator lights in the appropriate service information. List each of the warning indicators:**

2. **Turn the ignition to the "run" position (engine not running). List the status of each gauge/indicator:**

3. **Start the engine and allow it to run for a few minutes. List the status of each gauge/indicator:**

4. **List any gauges/indicators that are showing a fault and the fault indicated:**

5. **Have your supervisor/instructor verify satisfactory completion of this procedure, any observations found, and any necessary action(s) recommended.**

Performance Rating

CDX Tasksheet Number: C898

0	1	2	3	4

Supervisor/instructor signature _____ Date _____

▶ **TASK** Demonstrate awareness of the safety aspects of
supplemental restraint systems (SRS), electronic
brake control systems, and hybrid vehicle
high voltage circuits.

MAST
OA13

Time off_____

Time on_____

Total time_____

CDX Tasksheet Number: C464

1. **Research the following procedures for a hybrid vehicle in the appropriate service information.**

   a. **List the precautions when working around or on the SRS system on this vehicle:**

   b. **List the steps to disable the SRS system on this vehicle:**

   c. **List the steps to enable the SRS system on this vehicle:**

   d. **List the precautions when working on or around the electronic brake control system on this vehicle:**

e. Identify the high-voltage circuit wiring on this vehicle. What color is the wire conduit?

f. List or print out the high-voltage disable procedure for this vehicle.

2. Have your supervisor/instructor verify satisfactory completion of this task.

Performance Rating

CDX Tasksheet Number: C464

0	1	2	3	4

Supervisor/instructor signature _____ Date _____

Demonstrate awareness of the safety aspects of high voltage circuits (such as high-intensity discharge [HID] lamps, ignition systems, injection systems, etc.)

MAST
OA14

Time off_____

Time on_____

Total time_____

CDX Tasksheet Number: C895

Vehicle used for this activity:

Year _____ Make _____ Model _____

Odometer _____ VIN _____

1. **Using appropriate service information, identify system voltage and safety precautions associated with high-intensity discharge headlights, ignition systems, and injection systems.**

   a. **HID lamp voltage:** _____ **volts**

   b. **List the safety precautions required when working on HID system:**

   c. **Maximum secondary ignition system voltage:** _____ **volts**

   d. **List the safety precautions required when working around ignition systems:**

   e. **Injection system voltage (on a vehicle with a high-voltage injection system):** _____ **volts**

   f. **List the safety precautions required when working around high-voltage injection systems:**

2. **Have your supervisor/instructor verify satisfactory completion of this task.**

Performance Rating

CDX Tasksheet Number: C895

0	1	2	3	4

Supervisor/instructor signature _____ Date _____

Complete work order to include customer information, vehicle identifying information, customer concern, related service history, cause, and correction.

Time off_____

Time on_____

Total time_____

CDX Tasksheet Number: C885

1. **Using a vehicle with an engine-related customer concern, complete the work order, specifying the following:**

   a. **Customer information:**

   b. **Customer concern:**

   c. **Vehicle identifying information:**

   d. **Any related service history, etc.:**

2. **Determine the cause of the concern and list it on the work order.**

3. **List the action(s) needed to correct the concern, on the work order.**

4. **Have your supervisor/instructor verify satisfactory completion of the work order, any observations found, and any necessary action(s) recommended.**

Performance Rating

CDX Tasksheet Number: C885

0	1	2	3	4

Supervisor/instructor signature _____ Date _____

MAST
1A2

CDX Tasksheet Number: C002

1. **Using the VIN for identification, use the appropriate source to access the vehicle's service history in relation to prior related internal engine work or customer concerns.**

    a. **List any related repairs/concerns, and their dates:**

2. **Using the VIN for identification, access any relevant technical service bulletins for the particular vehicle you are working on in relation to any internal engine updates, precautions, or other service issues. List any related service bulletins and their titles:**

3. **Using the appropriate vehicle service information identify and list the correct fluid type for the vehicle.**

    a. **Engine oil**
    b. **Engine coolant**
    c. **Power steering fluid**
    d. **Brake fluid**
    e. **Clutch fluid**
    f. **Transmission fluid**
    g. **Diesel exhaust fluid**
    h. **Windshield washer fluid**

4. **Have your supervisor/instructor verify satisfactory completion of this procedure, any observations found, and any necessary action(s) recommended.**

> **NOTE** The following sign-off goes along with the first task on this tasksheet and can also be signed off once all of the other tasks in this tasksheet are completed.

Performance Rating

CDX Tasksheet Number: C002

0	1	2	3	4

Supervisor/instructor signature _____ Date _____

▶ **TASK** Identify service precautions related to service of the internal combustion engine of a hybrid vehicle.

MAST 1A9

Time off_____

Time on_____

Total time_____

CDX Tasksheet Number: C900

Vehicle used for this activity:

Year _____ Make _____ Model_____

Odometer_____ VIN_____

1. **Research the precautions when servicing an internal combustion engine on a hybrid vehicle in the appropriate service information. List all precautions:**

2. **Have your supervisor/instructor verify satisfactory completion of the procedure, any observations found, and any necessary action(s) recommended.**

Performance Rating

CDX Tasksheet Number: C900

0	1	2	3	4

Supervisor/instructor signature _____ Date _____

▶ **TASK** Demonstrate the use of the 3 Cs (concern, cause, and correction).

Additional Task

Time off_____

Time on_____

Total time_____

CDX Tasksheet Number: N/A

1. **Using the following scenario, write up the 3 Cs as listed on most repair orders. Assume that the customer authorized the recommended repairs.**

    An 8-year-old vehicle has been brought to your shop with an engine repair concern. The customer tells you that the vehicle runs rough at all speeds and conditions, and has gotten worse over the past couple of weeks. The malfunction indicator lamp (MIL) is blinking when the engine is running. The customer thought the malfunction was due to bad gas; he ran the tank out and refilled it with good gas from a very reputable station, but the car still runs rough after using half of a tank. The customer authorizes your shop to perform a diagnosis and you find the following:

    a. The vehicle is about 8 years old and has nearly 165,000 miles on it, but is in good overall condition.

    b. There is a diagnostic trouble code P0303, which indicates an engine misfire on cylinder #3.

    c. All of the spark plugs are moderately worn and show signs of moderate oil fouling, and the spark plug wires are original.

    d. Cylinder compression is about 25 psi on cylinder #3. The other cylinders are within specifications, but on the low side.

    e. A cylinder leakage test shows 85% leakage on cylinder #3 past the exhaust valve. The other cylinders show about 25% leakage past the piston rings.

    f. The engine mounts are oil-soaked due to a leaking valve cover and oil pan gaskets.

    g. The rear main seal shows signs of significant leakage.

    h. The oil light sometimes flickers when the engine is fully warmed up and Idling, even though the oil is near the full mark.

    i. The radiator has a small coolant leak in the core.

    NOTE Ask your instructor whether you should use a copy of the shop repair order or the 3 Cs in this manual to record this information.

2. **Concern:**

3. **Cause:**

4. **Correction:**

5. **Other recommended service:**

6. **Have your supervisor/instructor verify satisfactory completion of this procedure, any observations found, and any necessary action(s) recommended.**

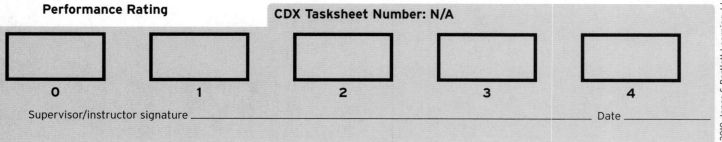

Performance Rating

CDX Tasksheet Number: N/A

0	1	2	3	4

Supervisor/instructor signature _____ Date _____

Perform cranking sound diagnosis.

Time off_____

Time on_____

CDX Tasksheet Number: N/A

1. **Disable the ignition or fuel system so that the engine will crank, but not start.**

Total time_____

> **NOTE** Some vehicles can be put into "clear flood" mode by depressing the throttle to the floor before turning the ignition key to the "run" position. This prevents the fuel injectors from being activated. If your vehicle is equipped with this mode, hold the throttle down to the floor and try cranking the engine over (make sure you are prepared to turn off the ignition switch if the engine starts). You can also disable the engine by disconnecting the fuel injectors or ignition coils.

2. **Crank the engine over for approximately 5 seconds and listen to the cranking sound.**

> **NOTE** The engine should crank over at a normal speed. Too fast could mean low compression caused by bent valves or a slipped timing belt or chain. Too slow could mean a seized piston or bearing, or a faulty starting system. An uneven cranking sound may indicate grossly uneven compression pressures in the cylinders.

3. **List your observation(s):**

4. **Determine any necessary action(s):**

5. **Have your supervisor/instructor verify satisfactory completion of this procedure, any observations found, and any necessary action(s) recommended.**

Performance Rating

CDX Tasksheet Number: N/A

0	1	2	3	4

Supervisor/instructor signature _____ Date _____

Perform engine absolute manifold pressure tests (vacuum/boost); determine needed action.

MAST
8A5

Time off_____

Time on_____

Total time_____

CDX Tasksheet Number: C392

1. **Find an appropriate vacuum hose to connect into.**

> **NOTE** Make sure the vacuum hose is connected to the intake manifold vacuum and you are not disconnecting anything that will affect the operation of the engine. If possible, the use of a vacuum tee will allow you to take the reading while allowing the vacuum to get to its intended device.

2. **Running Vacuum Test**

   a. **Describe the purpose of this test, the components or functions the test checks, and what the results might indicate:**

   b. **Start the engine, allow it to idle, and note the vacuum reading:**
   _____

      i. **Is the vacuum gauge needle relatively steady? Yes:** _____
         No: _____

   c. **Carefully raise the engine rpm to 2000 rpm and note the vacuum reading:** _____

      i. **Is the vacuum gauge needle relatively steady? Yes:** _____
         No: _____

      ii. **The vacuum reading should be higher at 2000 rpm than at idle. Is it?**
          Yes: _____ **No:** _____

   d. **Determine any necessary action(s):**

3. **Have your supervisor/instructor verify satisfactory completion of this procedure, any observations found, and any necessary action(s) recommended.**

Performance Rating

CDX Tasksheet Number: C392

0	1	2	3	4

Supervisor/instructor signature _____ Date _____

▶ **TASK** Perform cylinder power balance tests; determine needed action.

MAST
8A6

Time off_____

Time on_____

Total time_____

CDX Tasksheet Number: C393

1. Research the best option for disabling the cylinders on this vehicle in the appropriate service Information. The list that follows contains the most common methods. Choose the one that you plan on using.

   a. Disconnect individual spark plug wires or ignition coils. _____
   b. Disconnect individual fuel injectors (multi-port fuel injection only). _____
   c. Use a diagnostic scope to disable cylinders through the ignition primary circuit. _____
   d. Use a scan tool on vehicles with power balance capabilities. _____
   e. Use short sections of vacuum hose and a test light (option for waste spark ignition systems). _____

2. Determine from the service information if this vehicle has an idle control system. If it does, list how to best disable the system during this test:

3. Have your supervisor/instructor check the above answers. Supervisor's/instructor's initials: _____

4. If this vehicle is equipped with an idle control system, disable it and set the idle speed to an appropriate rpm.

   a. List the rpm here: _____

5. Disable the cylinders one at a time and record the rpm drop (not the rpm) of each cylinder.

   a. rpm drop: ---_____ ---_____ ---_____ ---_____ ---_____ ---_____ ---_____ ---_____

6. Determine any necessary action(s):

7. Have your supervisor/instructor verify satisfactory completion of this procedure, any observations found, and any necessary action(s) recommended.

Performance Rating

CDX Tasksheet Number: C393

0	1	2	3	4

Supervisor/instructor signature _____ Date _____

► TASK Perform cylinder cranking and running compression
tests; determine needed action.

MAST
8A7

Time off_____

Time on_____

Total time_____

CDX Tasksheet Number: C709

1. Research the procedure and specifications for performing both a cranking compression test and a running compression test on this vehicle in the appropriate service information.

2. List the conditions that must be met for the cranking compression test to be accurate (you may paraphrase):

3. Specifications

    a. Minimum compression pressure: _____ psi/kPa or %

    b. Maximum variation: _____ %

4. Cranking Compression Test: Perform the cranking compression test following the specified procedure. The top row in the table below is a standard test and the bottom row is a wet test using a small amount of clean engine oil. The wet test would normally be performed on engines that fail the standard test. List the readings obtained for each cylinder in the table.

Cylinder	#1	#2	#3	#4	#5	#6	#7	#8
Standard test (psi/kPa)								
Wet test(psi/kPa)								

    a. Calculate the difference between the highest and lowest cylinders (dry test): _____ %

5. Running Compression Test: Perform the running compression test following the specified procedure. List the readings obtained for each cylinder:

> **NOTE** Make sure the person snapping the throttle open is ready to turn off the ignition switch if the throttle sticks open.

Cylinder	#1	#2	#3	#4	#5	#6	#7	#8
Idle (psi/kPa)								
Snap throttle (psi/kPa)								

a. Determine any necessary action(s):

6. Have your supervisor/instructor verify satisfactory completion of this procedure, any observations found, and any necessary action(s) recommended.

Performance Rating

CDX Tasksheet Number: C709

0	1	2	3	4

Supervisor/instructor signature _____ Date _____

► **TASK** Perform cylinder leakage tests; determine needed action.

MAST
8A8

Time off_____

Time on_____

Total time_____

CDX Tasksheet Number: C395

1. List all of the possible places where compression can leak out of a cylinder:

2. Remove the appropriate spark plugs to test the cylinder with the lowest compression pressure.

3. Bring that piston up to top dead center on the compression stroke and install the cylinder leakage tester. List the reading you obtained.

    a. Cylinder #: _____

    b. Cylinder leakage: _____ %

    c. Leaking from: _____

4. Perform this test on one other cylinder. List the reading you obtained. Before removing the cylinder leakage tester, call your supervisor/instructor over to verify the reading.

    a. Cylinder #: _____

    b. Cylinder leakage: _____ %

    c. Leaking from: _____

5. Determine any necessary action(s):

6. Have your supervisor/instructor verify satisfactory completion of this procedure, any observations found, and any necessary action(s) recommended.

Performance Rating

CDX Tasksheet Number: C395

0	1	2	3	4

Supervisor/instructor signature _____ Date _____

Time off_____

Time on_____

Total time_____

CDX Tasksheet Number: C390

1. Ask your instructor to assign you a vehicle with an engine noise or vibration concern. List the customer concern:

2. Research possible causes of the concern for this vehicle in the appropriate service information.

   a. List any possible causes:

   b. List any specified tests to pinpoint the problem:

3. With your supervisor's/instructor's permission, operate the vehicle to verify the concern. List your observations:

4. Follow the service manual procedure to diagnose the concern. List your tests and results here:

5. Determine necessary action(s):

6. Have your supervisor/instructor verify satisfactory completion of this procedure, any observations found, and any necessary action(s) recommended.

Performance Rating

CDX Tasksheet Number: C390

0	1	2	3	4

Supervisor/instructor signature _____ Date _____

▶ **TASK** Inspect engine assembly for fuel, oil, coolant, and other leaks; determine needed action.

MAST
1A4

CDX Tasksheet Number: C004

> **NOTE** If the vehicle's engine assembly is coated with leaking fluids and road dirt, you may need to pressure wash the engine before inspecting it for leaks. Some very small leaks, or leaks on engines that have a lot of accumulated residue, may be diagnosed with the use of a fluorescent dye and ultraviolet light. Check with your supervisor/instructor about which procedure to perform. Follow the dye check equipment manufacturer's instructions if you are performing this test.

> **NOTE** Fluid leaks can be hard to locate. Remember that gravity tends to pull any leaking fluid down. You will need to identify the highest point of the leak to locate its source. Fluids can also be flung from rotating parts, sprayed under pressure from pinhole leaks, or blown by airflow far from the source. Investigate carefully.

1. **Check for fluid leaks under the hood. List any leaks (component leaking and type of fluid):**

2. **Safely raise and secure the vehicle on a hoist.**

3. **Inspect the engine, cooling system, fuel system, transmission/transaxle, and any differentials for leaks. Identify the type of fluid leaking and the source of the leak for the following items:**

   a. **Engine:**

   b. **Fuel system:**

   c. **Cooling system:**

d. Transmission/transaxle:

e. Steering system:

f. Differentials:

4. Determine any necessary action(s):

5. Have your supervisor/instructor verify satisfactory completion of this procedure, any observations found, and any necessary action(s) recommended.

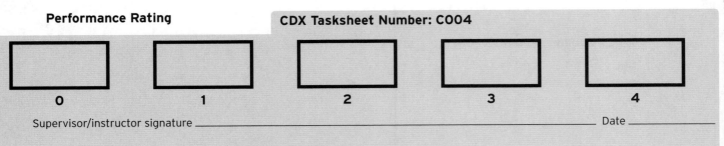

Performance Rating

CDX Tasksheet Number: C004

| 0 | 1 | 2 | 3 | 4 |

Supervisor/instructor signature _____ Date _____

▶ TASK Remove and reinstall engine on a newer vehicle equipped with OBD; reconnect all attaching components and restore the vehicle to running condition.

MAST
1A10

CDX Tasksheet Number: C671

1. **Research the procedure and specifications for removing and installing the engine in the appropriate service information.**

   a. **List the flat rate time for R&R engine:** _____ **hr**
   b. **List the flat rate time for R&R engine and O/H:** _____ **hr**
   c. **List any special tools required for this task:**

   d. **List the specified engine oil:** _____
   e. **List the engine oil capacity:** _____ **qt/lt**
   f. **List the specified coolant:** _____
   g. **List the cooling system capacity:** _____ **qt/lt**
   h. **List any precautions specific to replacing the engine in this vehicle:**

2. **Following the specified procedure(s), prepare the vehicle for engine removal by properly locating it in the work stall, draining any appropriate fluids such as engine coolant and oil, and removing any body components such as the hood, inner fender(s), etc.**

3. **Following the specified procedure(s), remove the engine assembly from the vehicle.**

4. **Inspect the assembly for any damaged components, fasteners, etc., and list your observation(s):**

5. **List the amount of time it took to remove the engine assembly:**
   _____ **hr**

6. **Have your supervisor/instructor verify removal of the engine assembly. Supervisor's/instructor's initials:** _____

> **NOTE** If you are rebuilding the engine, continue on to the Cylinder Head Removal, Inspection, and Installation tasksheet. After completion of those tasks, return here to reinstall the engine assembly.

7. Following the specified procedure(s) and specifications, reinstall the engine into the engine compartment.

8. Reconnect all hoses, wiring, belts, cables, and components, being careful to install them in their proper places.

9. Refill the engine with the specified oil. Ensure that the oil filter is installed.

10. Refill the cooling system with the specified coolant and bleed any air from the system.

11. Check all other fluid levels such as power steering fluid and brake fluid. Top off as necessary.

12. Recheck that all fasteners are properly torqued.

13. Perform any other prestart procedures such as charging the vehicle's battery, priming the lubrication system, etc.

14. List any specified break-in/start-up procedures:

15. Have your supervisor/instructor verify that the engine is ready to start. Supervisor's/instructor's initials: _____

> NOTE It is good practice to have a fire extinguisher close by in case of a fire.

16. Install the exhaust hose(s). Start the engine and check for proper oil pressure, leaks, and abnormal noises. If any problems arise, shut down the engine and repair any issues. List your observation(s):

17. Verify the proper adjustment of any timing components, if applicable.

18. Continue the break-in/start-up procedure, being careful to monitor the engine temperature, oil pressure, and malfunction indicator lamp (MIL). Stop the engine if any issues arise.

19. Once the initial break-in period is complete, shut down the engine and check for leaks, loose components, etc. List any observation(s):

20. Have your supervisor/instructor verify proper engine operation. Supervisor's/instructor's initials: _____

21. Reinstall any removed items such as the hood and inner fenders. Align as necessary.

22. Recheck the fluid levels and inspect for any leaks.

23. List the amount of time it took to install the engine assembly: _____ hr

24. With your instructor's permission, test drive the vehicle to verify correct operation. List your observation(s):

25. Have your supervisor/instructor verify satisfactory completion of this procedure, any observations found, and any necessary action(s) recommended.

Performance Rating

CDX Tasksheet Number: C671

0	1	2	3	4

Supervisor/instructor signature _____ Date _____

► **TASK** Remove, inspect, and/or replace crankshaft vibration damper (harmonic balancer).

MAST
1C1

Time off_____

Time on_____

Total time_____

CDX Tasksheet Number: C679

1. Research the procedure for removing and inspecting the crankshaft vibration damper in the appropriate service information.

    a. Specified crankshaft pulley bolt torque: _____ ft-lb/N·m
    b. List any special procedures or precautions related to the harmonic balancer:

2. Following the specified procedure, remove the harmonic balancer.

3. Following the specified procedure, inspect the harmonic balancer. List your observation(s):

4. Determine any necessary action(s):

5. Have your supervisor/instructor verify removal of the harmonic balancer and your answers. Supervisor/instructor: _____

> **NOTE** You may want to continue on with the next task at this point. If so, return to this task after reinstalling the timing components.

6. Following the specified procedure, reinstall the harmonic balancer.

7. Have your supervisor/instructor verify satisfactory completion of this procedure, any observations found, and any necessary action(s) recommended.

Performance Rating

CDX Tasksheet Number: C679

0	1	2	3	4

Supervisor/instructor signature _____ Date _____

Disassemble engine block; clean and prepare components for inspection and reassembly.

MAST
1C2

Time off_____

Time on_____

Total time_____

CDX Tasksheet Number: C029

1. **Research the procedure and specifications for disassembling and inspecting the engine block in the appropriate service information.**

    a. **Print off the procedure for disassembling the block and attach it to this sheet.**

    b. **List the specification for crankshaft end play: _____ in/mm**

> **NOTE** Make sure the engine stand is rated for the weight of the engine you are mounting on it. Also, use bolts with the proper strength and length. Severe injury could occur if the engine were to fall due to failure of the engine stand or bolts.

2. **If not already completed, mount the engine block to an appropriate engine stand. This may require the removal of the flex plate or flywheel.**

3. **Following the specified procedure, measure the crankshaft end play: _____ in/mm**

4. **Disassemble the engine block assembly following the specified procedure. Be sure to label all parts to identify where they will be reinstalled. As the engine is being disassembled, visually inspect the parts for obvious damage. List your observation(s):**

> **NOTE** Be very careful not to damage or scratch any aluminum sealing surfaces since doing so could cause a leak. Do not use metal scrapers, wire brushes, or power abrasive disks to clean aluminum or plastic surfaces.

5. **Remove any gasket material still stuck to the sealing surfaces with an approved scraper.**

6. **Clean the parts in a safe and environmentally approved way. This is commonly performed in a hot water spray machine.**

7. Visually inspect all parts. List your observation(s):

8. Have your supervisor/instructor verify satisfactory completion of this procedure, any observations found, and any necessary action(s) recommended.

Performance Rating

CDX Tasksheet Number: C029

0	1	2	3	4

Supervisor/instructor signature _____ Date _____

▶ **TASK** Inspect engine block for visible cracks, passage condition, core and gallery plug condition, and surface warpage; determine needed action.

Time off_____

Time on_____

Total time_____

CDX Tasksheet Number: C030

1. **Research the procedure and specifications for measuring the engine block for warpage in the appropriate service information.**

    a. **List the specification(s) for block deck warpage:**

2. **Following the specified procedure, carefully inspect the engine block for visible cracks (using magnaflux equipment or penetrating dyes). List your observation(s):**

3. **Inspect the condition of all passages. List your observation(s):**

> **NOTE** Core plugs are normally replaced during engine overhaul, so you may want to remove them at this time. Also, make sure the gallery plugs are removed for the cleaning process.

4. **Inspect the condition of core and gallery plugs. List your observation(s):**

5. **Inspect all sealing surfaces for damage. List your observation(s):**

6. **Determine any necessary action(s):**

7. **Have your supervisor/instructor verify satisfactory completion of this procedure, any observations found, and any necessary action(s) recommended.**

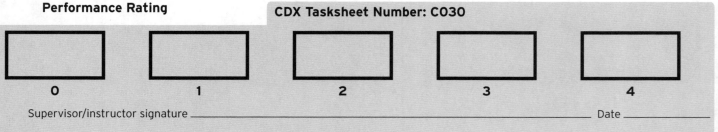

Performance Rating

CDX Tasksheet Number: C030

| 0 | 1 | 2 | 3 | 4 |

Supervisor/instructor signature _____ Date _____

MAST
1C5

Time off_____

Time on_____

Total time_____

CDX Tasksheet Number: C727

> **NOTE** This task should be performed only on engines that are not going to be machined over-size. Have your supervisor approve this task based on the results of the previous tasks before you continue.

1. **Is this cylinder block a good candidate for the deglazing process?**
   Yes: _____ **No:** _____

2. **Do you have your supervisor's approval for this task? Yes:** _____ **No:** _____

3. **Research the procedures and specifications for deglazing the cylinder walls.**
   a. **Specified coarseness of stones/ball hone:** _____
   b. **Specified deglazing lubricant:** _____
   c. **Specified crosshatch angle/pattern:** _____
   d. **Specified cleaning process after deglazing:** _____

4. **Following the specified procedure, carefully deglaze the cylinder walls using the appropriate honing/deglazing equipment.**

5. **Use the specified cleaning process to clean the cylinder walls and block.**

6. **Inspect the surface of the cylinders for proper deglazing finish. List your observation(s):**

7. **Have your supervisor/instructor verify satisfactory completion of this procedure, any observations found, and any necessary action(s) recommended.**

Performance Rating

CDX Tasksheet Number: C727

0	1	2	3	4

Supervisor/instructor signature _____ Date _____

► **TASK** Inspect crankshaft for straightness, journal damage, keyway damage, thrust flange and sealing surface condition, and visual surface cracks; check oil passage condition; measure end play and journal wear; check crankshaft position sensor reluctor ring (where applicable); determine needed action.

MAST
1C7

Time off_____

Time on_____

Total time_____

CDX Tasksheet Number: C728

1. **Research the procedure and specifications for inspecting the crankshaft and related parts in the appropriate service information.**

2. **Following the specified procedure, measure the crankshaft run-out (straightness).**

   a. **Specs:** _____ in/mm
   b. **Measurement:** _____ in/mm

3. **Following the specified procedure, visually inspect the following for damage, wear, or cracks. List your observations.**

   a. **Crankshaft main bearing journals: Worn _____ Damaged _____ Cracks _____ OK _____ (Check any that apply) Comments:**

   b. **Crankshaft rod bearing journals: Worn _____ Damaged _____ Cracks _____ OK _____ (Check any that apply) Comments:**

   c. **Crankshaft keyway: Worn _____ Damaged _____ Cracks _____ OK _____ (Check any that apply) Comments:**

   d. **Thrust flange: Worn _____ Damaged _____ Cracks _____ OK _____ (Check any that apply) Comments:**

   e. **Rear main bearing sealing surface: Worn _____ Damaged _____ Cracks _____ OK _____ (Check any that apply) Comments:**

f. Oil passages: Worn _____ Damaged _____ Cracks _____ OK _____
(Check any that apply) Comments:

g. Crankshaft position sensor reluctor ring: Worn _____ Damaged _____
Cracks _____ OK _____ (Check any that apply) Comments:

4. **Following the specified procedure, measure the crankshaft main bearing journals. List your measurements in the table below.**

Journal	Specs	#1	#2	#3	#4	#5	#6
Diameter (in/mm)							
Out-of-round (in/mm)							
Taper (in/mm)							

5. **Following the specified procedure, measure the crankshaft connecting rod journals. List your measurements in the table below.**

Journal	Specs	#1	#2	#3	#4	#5	#6	#7	#8
Diameter (in/mm)									
Out-of-round (in/mm)									
Taper (in/mm)									

6. **Determine any necessary action(s):**

7. **Have your supervisor/instructor verify satisfactory completion of this procedure, any observations found, and any necessary action(s) recommended.**

Performance Rating

CDX Tasksheet Number: C728

0	1	2	3	4

Supervisor/instructor signature _____ Date _____

© 2019 Jones & Bartlett Learning, LLC, an Ascend Learning Company

Inspect main and connecting rod bearings for damage and wear; determine needed action.

MAST
1C8

Time off_____

Time on_____

Total time_____

CDX Tasksheet Number: C036

1. **Research the procedure and specifications for inspecting the main and connecting rod bearings in the appropriate service information.**

    a. **List, or print off and attach to this sheet, the faults and wear patterns for the various bearing issues:**

2. **Following the specified procedure, inspect the main and connecting rod bearings. List your observations:**

3. **Determine any necessary action(s):**

4. **Have your supervisor/instructor verify satisfactory completion of this procedure, any observations found, and any necessary action(s) recommended.**

Performance Rating

CDX Tasksheet Number: C036

0	1	2	3	4

Supervisor/instructor signature _____ Date _____

▶ **TASK** Identify piston and bearing wear patterns that indicate connecting rod alignment and main bearing bore problems; determine needed action.

MAST
1C9

Time off_____

Time on_____

Total time_____

CDX Tasksheet Number: C729

1. **Research the procedure and specifications for inspecting the piston and bearing wear patterns in the appropriate service information.**

    a. **List, or print off and attach to this sheet, the faults and wear patterns for the various connecting rod and main bearing bore issues:**

2. **Following the specified procedure, visually inspect the pistons and bearings for abnormal wear patterns. List your observations:**

3. **Determine any necessary action(s):**

4. **Have your supervisor/instructor verify satisfactory completion of this procedure, any observations found, and any necessary action(s) recommended.**

Performance Rating

CDX Tasksheet Number: C729

0	1	2	3	4

Supervisor/instructor signature _____ Date _____

► **TASK** Inspect oil pump gears or rotors, housing, pressure relief devices, and pump drive; perform needed action.

MAST
1D13

Time off_____

Time on_____

Total time_____

CDX Tasksheet Number: C733

1. **Research the procedure and specifications to disassemble and inspect the oil pump in the appropriate service information.**

   a. **Type of oil pump:** _____

   b. **Regulated oil pressure:** _____ psi/kPa

   c. **List, or print off and attach to this sheet, the specified clearances for this pump:**

2. **Following the specified procedure, disassemble the pump and visually inspect the parts (including the pressure relief device and pump drive). List your observation(s):**

3. **Following the specified procedure, measure the pump clearances. List your findings:**

4. **Determine any necessary action(s):**

5. **Have your supervisor/instructor verify satisfactory completion of this procedure, any observations found, and any necessary action(s) recommended.**

Performance Rating

CDX Tasksheet Number: C733

0	1	2	3	4

Supervisor/instructor signature _____ Date _____

▶ TASK Inspect and measure cylinder walls/sleeves for damage, wear, and ridges; determine needed action.

MAST
1C4

Time off_____

Time on_____

Total time_____

CDX Tasksheet Number: C726

1. Research the procedures and specifications for inspecting and measuring the cylinder walls/sleeves in the appropriate service information.

    a. Specified cylinder bore diameter: _____ in/mm
    b. Specified cylinder bore maximum out-of-round: _____ in/mm
    c. Specified cylinder bore maximum taper: _____ in/mm

2. Following the specified procedure, carefully measure the diameter and the maximum out-of-round diameter for each cylinder bore. List your measurements in the table below.

Cylinder	#1	#2	#3	#4	#5	#6	#7	#8
Top (in/mm)								
Bottom (in/mm)								
Taper (in/mm)								
Out-of-round (in/mm)								

3. Following the specified procedure, carefully inspect the cylinder walls/sleeves for damage, wear, and ridges. List your observation(s):

4. Determine any necessary action(s):

5. Have your supervisor/instructor verify satisfactory completion of this procedure, any observations found, and any necessary action(s) recommended.

Performance Rating

CDX Tasksheet Number: C726

0	1	2	3	4

Supervisor/instructor signature _____ Date _____

Time off_____

Time on_____

Total time_____

CDX Tasksheet Number: C678

1. **Research the procedures and specifications for inspecting and measuring the piston skirts and ring lands in the appropriate service information.**

    a. **Specified piston skirt diameter:** _____ in/mm

    b. **Specified piston ring groove width**

       i. **Compression (top):** _____ in/mm

       ii. **Compression (bottom):** _____ in/mm

       iii. **Oil:** _____ in/mm

    c. **Specified piston-to-cylinder clearance:** _____ in/mm

2. **Inspect the piston surfaces for obvious signs of damage. List your observation(s):**

3. **Following the specified procedure, carefully measure the diameter, the piston-to-cylinder clearance, and the piston ring groove width (for top compression, bottom compression, and oil rings). List your measurements in the table below.**

Piston	#1	#2	#3	#4	#5	#6	#7	#8
Diameter (in/mm)								
Clearance (in/mm)								
Groove width (top) (in/mm)								
Groove width (bottom) (in/mm)								
Groove width (oil) (in/mm)								

4. **Are the pistons within specified tolerance?   Yes: _____ No: _____**

    a. **Why or why not?**

5. **Determine any necessary action(s):**

6. **Have your supervisor/instructor verify satisfactory completion of this procedure, any observations found, and any necessary action(s) recommended.**

© 2019 Jones & Bartlett Learning, LLC, an Ascend Learning Company

Performance Rating

CDX Tasksheet Number: C678

0	1	2	3	4

Supervisor/instructor signature _____ Date _____

Inspect auxiliary shaft(s) (balance, intermediate, idler, counterbalance, and/or silencer); inspect shaft(s) and support bearings for damage and wear; determine needed action; reinstall and time.

MAST
1C13

Time off_____

Time on_____

Total time_____

CDX Tasksheet Number: C730

1. Research the procedures and specifications to inspect any auxiliary shaft(s) and support bearings in the appropriate service information.

    a. List the type of shaft(s) this engine is equipped with:

    b. List any appropriate specification(s):

    c. List, or print off and attach to this sheet, the installation and timing procedure:

2. Inspect the auxiliary shaft(s) and support bearings. List your observation(s):

3. Determine any necessary action(s):

4. Have your supervisor/instructor check your answers.
   Supervisor/instructor initials: _____

5. Following the specified procedure, reinstall and time the auxiliary shaft(s).

6. Have your supervisor/instructor verify satisfactory completion of this procedure, any observations found, and any necessary action(s) recommended.

Performance Rating

CDX Tasksheet Number: C730

0	1	2	3	4

Supervisor/instructor signature _____ Date _____

Inspect and measure camshaft bearings for wear, damage, out-of-round, and alignment; determine needed action.

MAST
1C6

CDX Tasksheet Number: C034

> **NOTE** Perform this task only if the engine is a cam-in-block design. If it is an overhead cam design, the camshaft bearings are inspected during the Cylinder Head Disassembly, Inspection, and Repair tasksheet.

1. **Research the procedures and specifications for inspecting and measuring the camshaft bearings in the appropriate service information.**

    a. **Specified camshaft bearing inside diameter:** _____ **in/mm**

    b. **Specified camshaft journal diameter:** _____ **in/mm**

    c. **Specified camshaft journal bearing clearance:** _____ **in/mm**

    d. **Specified camshaft journal out-of-round (max):** _____ **in/mm**

2. **Inspect the condition of the cam lobes for excessive wear or damage. List your observation(s):**

3. **Measure the inside diameter of the camshaft bearings and the outside diameter of the cam journals. Calculate the bearing clearance and measure the maximum out-of-round reading for each camshaft journal. List your measurements in the table below.**

Cam Bearing or Journal	#1	#2	#3	#4	#5
Cam bearing diameter (in/mm)					
Cam journal diameter (in/mm)					
Bearing clearance (in/mm)					
Out-of-round (in/mm)					

4. **Inspect the bearings and journals for evidence of damage, wear, and misalignment. List your observation(s):**

5. **Determine any necessary action(s):**

6. Have your supervisor/instructor verify satisfactory completion of this procedure, any observations found, and any necessary action(s) recommended.

Performance Rating

CDX Tasksheet Number: CO34

0	1	2	3	4

Supervisor/instructor signature _____ Date _____

Determine piston-to-bore clearance.

MAST
1C11

Time off_____

Time on_____

Total time_____

CDX Tasksheet Number: C597

1. Research the procedure and specifications for determining the piston-to-bore clearance in the appropriate service information.

   a. Specified piston-to-bore clearance: _____ in/mm

2. Ensure the cylinder block is thoroughly cleaned according to the manufacturer's recommended procedure and is properly protected from rust and/or corrosion.

3. If the pistons have been replaced, follow the specified procedure to measure the piston-to-bore clearance for each piston and cylinder. List your measurements in the table below. If the bore and pistons are being reused, transfer the measurements from task C678, inspect and measure piston skirts and ring lands; determine needed action.

Cylinder	#1	#2	#3	#4	#5	#6	#7	#8
Piston-to-bore clearance (in/mm)								

4. Is the piston-to-bore clearance within the specified tolerance?
   Yes: _____ No: _____

5. Have your supervisor/instructor verify satisfactory completion of this procedure, any observations found, and any necessary action(s) recommended.

Performance Rating

CDX Tasksheet Number: C597

0	1	2	3	4

Supervisor/instructor signature _____ Date _____

MAST
1C12

Time off_____

Time on_____

Total time_____

CDX Tasksheet Number: C040

1. Research the procedure and specifications for inspecting, measuring, and installing piston rings in the appropriate service information.

    a. Specified piston ring end gap

        i. Top compression ring: _____ in/mm
        ii. Bottom compression ring: _____ in/mm
        iii. Oil ring: _____ in/mm

    b. List the markings or ring configuration that determine which side of the ring goes up.

        i. Top compression ring: _____
        ii. Bottom compression ring: _____
        iii. Oil ring: _____

    c. Draw, or print off and attach to this sheet, the specified position of each piston ring gap when installed on the piston:

2. Following the specified procedure, measure the piston ring end gap for each cylinder. List in the table below.

Cylinder	#1	#2	#3	#4	#5	#6	#7	#8
Top compression ring (in/mm)								
Bottom compression ring (in/mm)								
Oil ring (in/mm)								

    a. Do all of the piston ring end gaps meet specifications?
        Yes: _____ No: _____

3. If the end gaps meet specifications, install piston rings on each piston. Be sure each ring is placed in the proper ring groove and is installed with the correct side up and in the correct orientation around the piston.

4. Determine any necessary action(s):

5. Have your supervisor/instructor verify satisfactory completion of this procedure, any observations found, and any necessary action(s) recommended.

Performance Rating

CDX Tasksheet Number: C040

0	1	2	3	4

Supervisor/instructor signature _____ Date _____

CDX Tasksheet Number: C731

> **NOTE** Due to the differences in assembly procedures and specifications, it is recommended that the specified procedure and specifications be printed out and followed exactly.

> **NOTE** Most measurements were taken during the engine disassembly process to determine the necessary actions. Now that the engine is ready to be reassembled, all measurements need to be repeated to verify that parts are within their specified tolerances. Use the Engine Build Sheet to record all of your measurements. When provided to customers, it lends a touch of professionalism to the job.

1. **Reassemble the engine block following all manufacturer specifications and procedures. List the specifications in the CDX Engine Build/Spec Sheet. Be sure to verify the following information.**

    a. **Make sure the camshaft turns freely. If not, check for proper installation of the cam bearings.**

    b. **Check all oil gallery plugs, and make sure they are tightened/installed properly.**

    c. **Check all water jacket soft plugs for proper installation.**

    d. **Check crankshaft main journals for proper clearance, and record on the Engine Build/Spec Sheet.**

    e. **Check crankshaft end play, and record on the Engine Build/Spec Sheet.**

    f. **Clean and lubricate the cylinder walls. Lubricate the pistons and piston rings.**

    g. **Install the pistons with the rings in the proper orientation.**

    h. **Measure the connecting rod bearing clearance, and record on the Engine Build/Spec Sheet.**

    i. **Pack the oil pump with the proper lubricant and install the pump.**

2. **Once the block is assembled, list any observation(s):**

3. Have your supervisor/instructor verify satisfactory completion of this procedure, any observations found, and any necessary action(s) recommended.

> **NOTE** Once the block is assembled, return to the Cylinder Head Disassembly, Inspection, and Repair tasksheet to continue with the installation of the cylinder heads and valve timing components.

Performance Rating

CDX Tasksheet Number: C731

0	1	2	3	4

Supervisor/instructor signature _____ Date _____

© 2019 Jones & Bartlett Learning, LLC, an Ascend Learning Company

MAST
1B4

CDX Tasksheet Number: C723

1. On a vehicle with adjustable valves, research the procedure and specifications for adjusting the valves in the appropriate service information.

    a. List the type of lifters this engine uses: Mechanical: _____
Hydraulic: _____

    b. How are the valves adjusted on this engine?

    c. Specified valve clearance

       i. Intake: _____ in/mm @ _____ °F/°C

       ii. Exhaust: _____ in/mm @ _____ °F/°C

    d. Valve adjustment locknut torque, if equipped: _____ ft-lb/N·m

2. Following the specified procedure, adjust the valves to specification. List your observation(s):

3. Determine any necessary action(s):

4. Have your supervisor/instructor verify satisfactory completion of this procedure, any observations found, and any necessary action(s) recommended.

Performance Rating

CDX Tasksheet Number: C723

0	1	2	3	4

Supervisor/instructor signature _____ Date _____

Time off_____

Time on_____

Total time_____

CDX Tasksheet Number: C541

> **NOTE** This task may be completed as part of an engine rebuild or done separately
> on another vehicle.

1. **List the gaskets and/or seals you are installing:**

2. **Research the procedure and specifications for the gaskets and/or seals you are
   removing/installing in the appropriate service information.**

   a. **List the recommended sealant required for each gasket/seal, if needed:**

   b. **List or print off and attach to this sheet any torque specifications for the
      cover(s) you are removing:**

3. **Following the specified procedure, remove the appropriate engine cover.**

4. **Remove any seals and gasket material with the proper tools. Be careful not
   to gouge or damage the surfaces being cleaned. Also, prepare the sealing
   surfaces for cover reinstallation according to the service information. List your
   observation(s):**

5. Have your supervisor/instructor verify that the cover is ready to be reinstalled. Supervisor's/instructor's initials: _____

6. Reinstall the cover following the specified procedure. Torque all fasteners to the proper torque and check for any leakage.

7. Have your supervisor/instructor verify satisfactory completion of this procedure, any observations found, and any necessary action(s) recommended.

Performance Rating

CDX Tasksheet Number: C541

0	1	2	3	4

Supervisor/instructor signature _____ Date _____

© 2019 Jones & Bartlett Learning, LLC, an Ascend Learning Company

► TASK Inspect, remove, and/or replace engine mounts.

MAST
1A8

Time off_____

Time on_____

Total time_____

CDX Tasksheet Number: C596

1. Research the procedure to inspect and replace the engine mounts in the appropriate service information.

   a. List the type of engine mount this vehicle uses: _____

   b. List or print off and attach to this sheet the precautions for performing this task:

   c. List or print off and attach to this sheet the procedure for inspecting the engine mounts:

2. Following the specified procedure, inspect the engine mounts and list your observations:

3. Determine any necessary action(s):

4. Have your supervisor/instructor verify your answers and initial if correct. Supervisor's/instructor's initials: _____

5. With your instructor's permission, remove one or more engine mounts following the specified procedure. Inspect the removed engine mount(s) and list your observations:

© 2019 Jones & Bartlett Learning, LLC, an Ascend Learning Company

Engine Repair   **141**

6. Have your supervisor/instructor verify the removal of the mount. Supervisor's/instructor's initials: _____

7. Reinstall the engine mount(s) according to the specified procedure.

8. Determine any necessary action(s):

9. Have your supervisor/instructor verify satisfactory completion of this procedure, any observations found, and any necessary action(s) recommended.

Performance Rating

CDX Tasksheet Number: C596

0	1	2	3	4

Supervisor/instructor signature _____ Date _____

MAST
1A6

Time off_____

Time on_____

Total time_____

CDX Tasksheet Number: C899

1. Research the procedure and specifications for inspecting and replacing the timing belt components in the appropriate service information.

    a. List the recommended change interval for the timing belt:
_____ mi/km

    b. List the flat rate time for removing and replacing the timing belt:
_____ hrs

    c. What other components does the manufacturer recommend changing at the same time as the timing belt?

    d. List or print off and attach the steps for removing and replacing the timing belt:

        i. Supervisor's/instructor's initials verifying approval to remove this timing belt: _____

2. With your instructor's permission, and following the specified steps, remove the timing belt.

3. Inspect the belt, pulleys, tensioner, cam seals, and water pump. List your observations for each:

4. Have your instructor verify removal of the timing belt and your observations:
_____

5. Following the specified procedure, reinstall the timing belt, making sure the timing marks are properly aligned and the belt is properly tensioned. Do not install the timing cover yet.

6. **Have your instructor verify installation of the timing belt and camshaft timing:**

   _____

7. **Reassemble any removed components and belts being careful to properly tighten all fasteners and accessory drive belts.**

8. **When everything is back together, carefully turn the engine by hand (ignition key off) at least two complete turns to verify there isn't a piston-to-valve interference.**

9. **If the engine turns over properly, start the engine, verify it is running properly, and make any timing or other adjustments.**

10. **Have your supervisor/instructor verify satisfactory completion of this procedure, any observations found, and any necessary action(s) recommended.**

Performance Rating

CDX Tasksheet Number: C899

| 0 | 1 | 2 | 3 | 4 |

Supervisor/instructor signature _____ Date _____

▶ TASK Inspect and replace camshaft and drive belt/chain (includes checking drive gear wear and backlash, endplay, sprocket and chain wear, overhead cam drive sprocket[s], drive belt[s], belt tension, tensioners, camshaft reluctor ring/tone-wheel, and variable valve timing components); verify correct camshaft timing.

MAST
1B5

Time off_____

Time on_____

Total time_____

CDX Tasksheet Number: C676

1. **Research the procedure and specifications for inspecting and replacing the camshaft and timing components in the appropriate service information.**

    a. **Type of cam drive system used:** _____

    b. **Is this engine equipped with variable valve timing? Yes:** _____
    No: _____

    c. **Camshaft endplay:** _____ **in/mm**

    d. **Camshaft drive gear backlash, if equipped:** _____ **in/mm**

    e. **List or print off and attach to this sheet any precautions when performing this task:**

    f. **List or print off and attach to this sheet any measurement and torque specifications for this task:**

2. **Following the specified procedure, remove any timing belt/chain covers. Visually inspect the installed timing components, including belt/chain tensioner. List your observations:**

3. **Following the specified procedure, disassemble the cam drive system. Clean all gasket surfaces.**

4. **Inspect the condition of the following components, if equipped, and list your observations:**

    a. **Timing belt/chain:** _____

    b. **Sprockets:** _____

    c. **Belt/chain tensioners:** _____

    d. Camshaft endplay: _____ in/mm

    e. Camshaft drive-gear backlash: _____ in/mm

    f. Camshaft reluctor ring/tone-wheel: _____

    g. Crank and cam oil seals: _____

    h. Water pump: _____

    i. Variable valve timing components: _____

5. Determine any necessary action(s):

6. Have your instructor verify removal of the timing components and your observations: _____

7. Following the specified procedure, reinstall the timing components, making sure the timing marks are properly aligned and the belt or chain is properly tensioned. Do not install the timing cover yet.

8. Have your instructor verify installation of the timing components and camshaft timing: _____

9. Reassemble any removed components and belts, being careful to properly tighten all fasteners and accessory drive belts.

10. When everything is back together, carefully turn the engine by hand (ignition key off) at least two complete turns to verify there isn't a piston-to-valve interference.

11. If the engine turns over properly, start the engine, verify it is running properly, and make any timing or other adjustments.

12. Have your supervisor/instructor verify satisfactory completion of this procedure, any observations found, and any necessary action(s) recommended.

Performance Rating

CDX Tasksheet Number: C676

0	1	2	3	4

Supervisor/instructor signature _____ Date _____

© 2019 Jones & Bartlett Learning, LLC, an Ascend Learning Company

MAST
1B6

CDX Tasksheet Number: C677

> **NOTE** If not already done, install the timing components following the specified procedure, being careful to line up all timing marks. Also, ensure that all belts/chains are properly tensioned.

1. **Research the procedure and specifications to establish camshaft position indexing in the appropriate service information.**

   a. **List, or print off and attach to this sheet, the procedure for indexing the camshaft position sensor:**

2. **Following the specified procedure, index the camshaft position sensor. List your observation(s):**

3. **Have your supervisor/instructor verify satisfactory completion of this procedure, any observations found, and any necessary action(s) recommended.**

Performance Rating

CDX Tasksheet Number: C677

0	1	2	3	4

Supervisor/instructor signature _____ Date _____

Replace valve stem seals on an assembled engine; inspect valve spring retainers, locks/keepers, and valve lock/keeper grooves; determine needed action.

MAST
1B8

Time off_____

Time on_____

Total time_____

CDX Tasksheet Number: C675

1. **Research the procedures and specifications for replacing the valve stem seals while the engine is installed in the vehicle in the appropriate service information.**

   a. **List, or print off and attach to this sheet, the precautions for performing this task:**

   b. **List the type of valve seals this engine is equipped with:** _____

   c. **List the flat rate time to perform this task:** _____ hr

   d. **List the special tools required to perform this task:**

2. **Have your supervisor/instructor verify your answers and initial. Supervisor/instructor's initials:** _____

3. **Following the specified procedure, prepare the engine for removal of the valve spring keepers and retainer by removing the valve cover and rocker arm or cam follower (some engines may require removal of the cam).**

4. **With the valve firmly held in place with compressed air, tap the valve retainer with a hammer and socket to break the bond between the retainer and keepers. Tap in line with the valve stem; do not tap sideways because that could bend the valve stem.**

5. **Install the valve spring compressor and compress the valve spring. Remove the keepers; be sure not to let them fall into the engine. Remove the valve spring and retainer.**

6. **Check to see if there is a burr on the valve stem near the keeper groove. File it smooth if necessary. Remove the old valve seal. Install the new valve seal according to the specified procedure. This may include using a sleeve that fits over the valve stem to protect the valve seal during installation. Also lubricate the seal before installation. And make sure it is fully seated if it is of the positive seal type.**

7. Reinstall the valve spring, retainer, and keepers. Be sure to seat the keepers fully in the valve stem groove.

8. Have your supervisor/instructor verify correct installation of the valve seals and springs. Supervisor/instructor's initials: _____

9. Reinstall the removed valve cover(s) and other parts.

10. Start the engine and verify correct operation.

11. Have your supervisor/instructor verify satisfactory completion of this procedure, any observations found, and any necessary action(s) recommended.

Performance Rating

CDX Tasksheet Number: C675

0	1	2	3	4

Supervisor/instructor signature _____ Date _____

► **TASK** Remove cylinder head; inspect gasket condition; install cylinder head and gasket; tighten according to manufacturer's specification and procedure.

MAST
1B1

Time off_____

Time on_____

Total time_____

CDX Tasksheet Number: C673

1. **Research the procedure and specifications for removing and installing the cylinder head(s) in the appropriate service information.**

   a. **Does this vehicle use TTY head bolts? Yes: _____ No: _____**

   b. **List or print off and attach to this sheet any special tools required for this task:**

   c. **List or print off and attach to this sheet any special precautions required for this task:**

   d. **List or print off and attach to this sheet the straightness specifications for the head surface:**

   e. **List or print off and attach to this sheet the surface finish requirements for the head surface:**

   f. **List or print off and attach to this sheet the torque procedure for the head bolts:**

g. **Draw or print off and attach to this sheet the torque sequence for the head bolts:**

2. **Following the specified procedure, remove the cylinder head(s).**

> **NOTE** Be very careful not to damage or scratch the head surface as this could cause a leak. Lay the head down on shop towels, and only use nonmetallic scrapers on aluminum or plastic surfaces.

3. **Inspect the old gasket(s) and list your observation(s):**

> **NOTE** While the head(s) is(are) removed from the engine, it makes sense to perform task C674: Clean and visually inspect a cylinder head for cracks; check gasket surface areas for warpage and surface finish; check passage condition.

4. **Following the procedure in the service information, install the head gasket(s) and cylinder head(s). Make sure you follow the specified procedure and sequence for tightening down the head bolts. Failure to do so could cause the gasket to fail.**

5. **Have your supervisor/instructor verify satisfactory completion of this procedure, any observations found, and any necessary action(s) recommended.**

Performance Rating

CDX Tasksheet Number: C673

0	1	2	3	4

Supervisor/instructor signature _____ Date _____

© 2019 Jones & Bartlett Learning, LLC, an Ascend Learning Company

▶ TASK Clean and visually inspect a cylinder head for cracks; check gasket surface areas for warpage and surface finish; check passage condition.

MAST
1B2

Time off_____

Time on_____

Total time_____

CDX Tasksheet Number: C674

1. **Following the procedure in the service information, clean the head surfaces and prepare them for inspection.**

> **NOTE** Be very careful not to damage or scratch the head surface as this could cause a leak. Lay the head down on shop towels, and only use nonmetallic scrapers on aluminum or plastic surfaces.

2. **Inspect the heads for signs of any cracks. This may involve magnafluxing or chemical crack detection. List the procedure you used and any observation(s):**

3. **Measure the gasket surfaces for warpage. List your measurements and observation(s):**

4. **Check the surface finish according to the manufacturer's procedure. List your observation(s):**

5. **Inspect the passages for blockage or leakage. List your observation(s):**

6. **Have your supervisor/instructor verify satisfactory completion of this procedure, any observations found, and any necessary action(s) recommended.**

Performance Rating

CDX Tasksheet Number: C674

0	1	2	3	4

Supervisor/instructor signature _____ Date _____

MAST
1B10

CDX Tasksheet Number: C720

1. **Research the procedure and specifications for inspecting valves and valve seats in the appropriate service information.**

   a. **Specified valve stem diameter**

       i. **Intake:** _____ in/mm

       ii. **Exhaust:** _____ in/mm

   b. **Specified valve margin thickness**

       i. **Intake:** _____ in/mm

       ii. **Exhaust:** _____ in/mm

   c. **Specified valve face angle**

       i. **Intake:** _____ degrees

       ii. **Exhaust:** _____ degrees

   d. **Specified valve seat angle**

       i. **Intake:** _____ degrees

       ii. **Exhaust:** _____ degrees

   e. **Specified valve seat width**

       i. **Intake:** _____ in/mm

       ii. **Exhaust:** _____ in/mm

   f. **List, or print off and attach to this sheet, the procedure for inspecting the valves and valve seats:**

2. **Measure the valve stem diameter and check for taper. List your measurements in the table below.**

Valve	#1	#2	#3	#4	#5	#6	#7	#8
Intake (in/mm)								
Exhaust (in/mm)								

3. **Measure the valve margin thickness. List your measurements in the table below.**

Valve	#1	#2	#3	#4	#5	#6	#7	#8
Intake (in/mm)								
Exhaust (in/mm)								

4. **Measure the valve seat width. List your measurements in the table below.**

Valve Seat	#1	#2	#3	#4	#5	#6	#7	#8
Intake (in/mm)								
Exhaust (in/mm)								

5. **Inspect the valves and valve seats according to the manufacturer's procedure. List your observation(s):**

6. **Determine any necessary action(s):**

7. **Have your supervisor/instructor verify satisfactory completion of this procedure, any observations found, and any necessary action(s) recommended.**

Performance Rating

CDX Tasksheet Number: C720

| 0 | 1 | 2 | 3 | 4 |

Supervisor/instructor signature _____ Date _____

MAST
1B9

CDX Tasksheet Number: C719

1. Research the procedure and specifications for checking valve guides and clearance in the appropriate service information.

    a. Specified valve guide clearance

        i. Intake: _____ in/mm

        ii. Exhaust: _____ in/mm

    b. Which method of determining valve guide clearance is recommended? Micrometer method / Dial indicator method (Circle one)

2. Measure the intake valve guide inner diameter and the intake valve stem diameter; calculate the clearance (micrometer method) or measure the side-to-side play of the valve stem with a dial indicator (dial indicator method). List your measurements in the table below.

Intake Valve	#1	#2	#3	#4	#5	#6	#7	#8
Guide (in/mm)								
Valve (in/mm)								
Clearance (in/mm)								

3. Measure the exhaust valve guide inner diameter and the exhaust valve stem diameter, then calculate the clearance (micrometer method), or measure the side-to-side play of the valve stem with a dial indicator (dial indicator method). List your measurements in the table below.

Exhaust Valve	#1	#2	#3	#4	#5	#6	#7	#8
Guide (in/mm)								
Valve (in/mm)								
Clearance (in/mm)								

4. Determine any necessary action(s):

5. Have your supervisor/instructor verify satisfactory completion of this procedure, any observations found, and any necessary action(s) recommended.

Performance Rating

CDX Tasksheet Number: C719

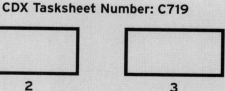

| 0 | 1 | 2 | 3 | 4 |

Supervisor/instructor signature _____ Date _____

► **TASK** Inspect valve springs for squareness and free height comparison; determine needed action.

CDX Tasksheet Number: C718

MAST
1B7

1. Research the procedure and specifications for checking valve spring squareness and free height in the appropriate service information.

    a. List, or print off and attach to this sheet, the procedure for checking squareness:

    b. Specified valve spring free height
       i. Intake: _____ in/mm
       ii. Exhaust: _____ in/mm

    c. Specified valve spring installed height
       i. Intake: _____ in/mm
       ii. Exhaust: _____ in/mm

    d. Specified valve spring pressure at the specified installed height
       i. Intake: _____ lb/kg at
       _____ in/mm
       ii. Exhaust: _____ lb/kg at
       _____ in/mm

    e. Specified valve spring pressure at the specified valve open height
       i. Intake: _____ lb/kg at
       _____ in/mm
       ii. Exhaust: _____ lb/kg at
       _____ in/mm

> **NOTE** You may want to measure and record the existing valve installed height and valve stem height before grinding the valves or machining the valve seats since specifications are not always available. Since some engines have nonadjustable valve trains, this is a critical measurement when reassembling the valve assemblies.

2. Disassemble the valve and valve spring assemblies, if not already done.

3. Check the valve springs for squareness using the protractor-head square. List your observation(s):

4. **Measure the free height of each valve spring. List your measurements in the table below.**

Valve Spring	#1	#2	#3	#4	#5	#6	#7	#8
Intake (in/mm)								
Exhaust (in/mm)								

5. **Measure the valve spring pressure at the specified installed height. List your measurements in the table below.**

Valve Spring	#1	#2	#3	#4	#5	#6	#7	#8
Intake (lb/kg)								
Exhaust (lb/kg)								

6. **Measure the valve spring pressure at the specified valve open height. List your measurements in the table below.**

Valve Spring	#1	#2	#3	#4	#5	#6	#7	#8
Intake (lb/kg)								
Exhaust (lb/kg)								

7. **Determine any necessary action(s):**

8. **Have your supervisor/instructor verify satisfactory completion of this procedure, any observations found, and any necessary action(s) recommended.**

Performance Rating

0	1	2	3	4

Supervisor/instructor signature _____ Date _____

▶ TASK Check valve spring assembled height and valve stem height; determine needed action.

CDX Tasksheet Number: C721

MAST
1B11

1. **Research the procedure and specifications in the appropriate service information for checking the following:**

    a. **Specified valve stem height**

        i. **Intake:** _____ **in/mm**

        ii. **Exhaust:** _____ **in/mm**

    b. **Specified valve spring assembled height**

        i. **Intake:** _____ **in/mm**

        ii. **Exhaust:** _____ **in/mm**

    c. **List, or print off and attach to this sheet, the procedure for making these measurements:**

2. **Perform this task only if the valves and valve seats are ready to be put back into service.**

> **NOTE** The valves are ready to be put back into service if they have been reground to meet specifications or if they have been replaced with new valves. This also applies for the valve seats. If you sent the heads out to be machined, the machinist should have ensured that these specifications were met.

3. **Measure the valve stem height. List your measurements in the table below.**

Valve	#1	#2	#3	#4	#5	#6	#7	#8
Intake (in/mm)								
Exhaust (in/mm)								

4. **Measure the valve spring assembled height. List your measurements in the table below.**

> **NOTE** If the valve springs have been replaced with new ones, double-check the valve spring pressure to make sure they meet specifications. If you are reusing the existing valve springs and they passed this test earlier, continue on.

Valve	#1	#2	#3	#4	#5	#6	#7	#8
Intake (in/mm)								
Exhaust (in/mm)								

5. **Determine any necessary action(s):**

6. **Have your supervisor/instructor verify satisfactory completion of this procedure, any observations found, and any necessary action(s) recommended.**

> **NOTE** NATEF has not specified a task for reassembling the head(s). However, now would be a good time to do so. Follow the specified procedure to reassemble the head(s), but be sure to follow all the necessary precautions.

> **NOTE** Some overhead cam heads with bucket-style cam followers may need to have their valves adjusted at this point with the use of select fit shims. Check the service information to determine if this procedure is required for this engine. If so, adjust the valve at this time. Otherwise, valve adjustment will happen after the head and timing components have been installed.

Performance Rating

CDX Tasksheet Number: C721

0	1	2	3	4

Supervisor/instructor signature _____ Date _____

► **TASK** Inspect pushrods, rocker arms, rocker arm pivots, and shafts for wear, bending, cracks, looseness, and blocked oil passages (orifices); determine needed action.

MAST
1B3

Time off_____

Time on_____

Total time_____

CDX Tasksheet Number: C021

1. Research the procedure and specifications for disassembling and inspecting the pushrods, rocker arms, pivots, and shafts in the appropriate service information.

   a. List, or print off and attach to this sheet, the procedure for inspecting these parts:

2. Disassemble the rocker arm assemblies and clean them in a safe and environmentally approved way. This is commonly performed in a hot water spray machine.

3. Inspect the following parts:

   a. Pushrods: Worn _____ Bent _____ Cracked _____ Blocked passages _____ OK _____ (Check any that apply)

   b. Rocker arms: Worn _____ Bent _____ Cracked _____ Blocked passages _____ OK _____ (Check any that apply)

   c. Rocker arm studs: Worn _____ Bent _____ Cracked _____ OK _____ (Check any that apply)

   d. Pivots/shafts: Worn _____ Bent _____ Cracked _____ Blocked passages _____ OK _____ (Check any that apply)

4. Determine any necessary action(s):

5. Have your supervisor/instructor verify satisfactory completion of this procedure, any observations found, and any necessary action(s) recommended.

Performance Rating

CDX Tasksheet Number: C021

0	1	2	3	4

Supervisor/instructor signature _____ Date _____

▶ **TASK** Inspect valve lifters; determine needed action.

MAST
1B12

CDX Tasksheet Number: C722

Time off_____

Time on_____

Total time_____

1. Research the procedure and specifications for inspecting the valve lifters in the appropriate service information.

   a. List the type of lifter this engine is equipped with:
      Hydraulic _____ Solid _____

   b. List, or print off and attach to this sheet, the inspection procedure and any specifications:

2. Inspect the valve lifters and list your observation(s):

3. Determine any necessary action(s):

4. Have your supervisor/instructor verify satisfactory completion of this procedure, any observations found, and any necessary action(s) recommended.

Performance Rating

CDX Tasksheet Number: C722

0	1	2	3	4

Supervisor/instructor signature _____ Date _____

© 2019 Jones & Bartlett Learning, LLC, an Ascend Learning Company

▶ **TASK** Inspect and/or measure camshaft for runout, journal wear, and lobe wear.

MAST
1B13

CDX Tasksheet Number: C724

1. Research the procedure and specifications for inspecting and measuring the camshaft in the appropriate service information.

    a. Specified maximum camshaft journal runout: _____ in/mm
    b. Specified camshaft journal diameter: _____ in/mm
    c. Specified lobe lift
       i. Intake: _____ in/mm
       ii. Exhaust: _____ in/mm
    d. Specified maximum lobe wear: _____ in/mm

2. Visually inspect the condition of the cam lobes for excessive wear. List your observation(s):

3. Following the specified procedure, measure the camshaft journal runout. List the measurement. List which journals were supported and which one was measured.

4. Following the specified procedure, measure the camshaft journal diameter. List your measurements for each cam journal in the table below.

Camshaft Journal	#1	#2	#3	#4	#5
Cam #1 (in/mm)					
Cam #2 (in/mm)					
Cam #3 (in/mm)					
Cam #4 (in/mm)					

5. Calculate the maximum camshaft journal wear: _____ in/mm

6. Following the specified procedure, measure the cam lobe lift and list your measurements in the table below.

	#1	#2	#3	#4	#5	#6	#7	#8
Intake lobes								
Exhaust Lobes								

7. Calculate the maximum lobe wear.

    a. Intake: _____ in/mm
    b. Exhaust: _____ in/mm

8. Determine any necessary action(s):

9. Have your supervisor/instructor verify satisfactory completion of this procedure, any observations found, and any necessary action(s) recommended.

Performance Rating

CDX Tasksheet Number: C724

0	1	2	3	4

Supervisor/instructor signature _____ Date _____

► **TASK** Inspect camshaft bearing surface for wear, damage, out-of-round, and alignment; determine needed action.

MAST
1B14

Time off_____

Time on_____

Total time_____

CDX Tasksheet Number: C027

> **NOTE** Perform this task only if the engine is an overhead cam design. If it is a cam-in-block design, the camshaft bearings are inspected during the Block Disassembly, Inspection, and Repair tasksheet.

1. **Research the procedures and specifications for inspecting and measuring the camshaft bearings in the appropriate service information.**

    a. **Specified camshaft bearing inside diameter:** _____ in/mm
    b. **Specified camshaft journal diameter:** _____ in/mm
    c. **Specified camshaft journal bearing clearance:** _____ in/mm

2. **Measure the inside diameter of the camshaft bearings. List your measurements in the table below.**

Camshaft Bearing	#1	#2	#3	#4	#5
Cam #1 (in/mm)					
Cam #2 (in/mm)					
Cam #3 (in/mm)					
Cam #4 (in/mm)					

3. **Measure the diameter of the camshaft journals (or copy them from the previous task). List your measurements in the table below.**

Camshaft Journal	#1	#2	#3	#4	#5
Cam #1 (in/mm)					
Cam #2 (in/mm)					
Cam #3 (in/mm)					
Cam #4 (in/mm)					

4. **Calculate the camshaft journal bearing clearance. List your measurements in the table below.**

Camshaft Journal	#1	#2	#3	#4	#5
Cam #1 (in/mm)					
Cam #2 (in/mm)					
Cam #3 (in/mm)					
Cam #4 (in/mm)					

5. **Inspect the bearings and journals for evidence of damage, wear, and misalignment. List your observation(s):**

6. **Determine any necessary action(s):**

7. **Have your supervisor/instructor verify satisfactory completion of this procedure, any observations found, and any necessary action(s) recommended.**

Performance Rating

CDX Tasksheet Number: CO27

0	1	2	3	4

Supervisor/instructor signature _____ Date _____

© 2019 Jones & Bartlett Learning, LLC, an Ascend Learning Company

▶ **TASK** Perform engine oil and filter change; use proper fluid type per manufacturer specification.

MAST
1D10

Time off_____

Time on_____

Total time_____

CDX Tasksheet Number: C737

1. **Research the following specifications/procedures for this vehicle in the appropriate service information.**

    a. **Oil capacity:** _____ qt/lt

    b. **Oil viscosity:** _____

    c. **API or other specified rating:** _____

    d. **Oil pan drain plug torque:** _____ ft-lb/N·m

    e. **Oil filter part number:** _____

    f. **List any special requirements/procedures for changing the oil and filter on this vehicle:**

NOTE Some vehicles have more than one oil drain plug and/or a special procedure for changing the filter.

---

    g. **Determine that a new filter, and the proper oil, is available for this vehicle before proceeding.   Yes:** _____ **No:** _____

2. **Safely raise and secure the vehicle on a hoist.**

NOTE Removing the oil filler cap may allow the oil to drain faster.

---

3. **Follow the specified procedure for draining the used oil and removing the old oil filter.**

NOTE The oil may be extremely hot. Be sure not to come into contact with the used oil.

---

    a. **Is the drain plug gasket reusable? Yes:** _____ **No:** _____

    b. **Did the oil filter gasket come off with the oil filter? Yes:** _____
    No: _____

    c. **Have your instructor verify these answers by initialing here:** _____

4. **Once the used oil has been drained, follow the manufacturer's procedure for installing the new oil filter (oil the gasket) and reinstalling the drain plug (tighten to the specified torque).**

5. **Lower the vehicle.**

6. **Following the appropriate service information, add the proper amount of new oil.**

7. Prepare to start the vehicle by applying the parking brake and placing exhaust hoses over the exhaust pipe(s). Start the vehicle and check for oil leaks. If oil leaks are found, shut off the engine immediately, locate the source of the leak, and inform your instructor. If no leaks are found, shut off the engine after a minute or two of running.

8. Let the engine oil drain back into the oil pan for a few minutes and then check to see that the oil is at the proper level. Add oil if necessary.

   a. What is the final oil level? _____

9. Dispose of the old oil and filter according to legislative guidelines (national, federal, state, and local).

10. Reset the maintenance reminder system if equipped, or fill out an oil-change reminder sticker and place it on the vehicle according to your shop's policy.

11. Have your supervisor/instructor verify satisfactory completion of this procedure, any observations found, and any necessary action(s) recommended.

Performance Rating

CDX Tasksheet Number: C737

0	1	2	3	4

Supervisor/instructor signature _____ Date _____

© 2019 Jones & Bartlett Learning, LLC, an Ascend Learning Company

MAST
6F3

Time off_____

Time on_____

Total time_____

CDX Tasksheet Number: C1003

1. **Research the description and operation of each maintenance indicator and the procedure for resetting the maintenance indicators in the appropriate service information. List each of the maintenance indicators and the reset procedure:**

2. **Turn the ignition switch to the on/run position (Key On, Engine Off-KOEO). List the status of each maintenance indicator:**

3. **Start the engine and allow it to run for a few minutes. List the status of each maintenance indicator:**

4. **List any maintenance indicators that are showing required maintenance:**

5. **Ask your supervisor/instructor if you should carry out the reset procedure for any maintenance indicators that are showing required maintenance.**

6. Have your supervisor/instructor verify satisfactory completion of this procedure, any observations found, and any necessary action(s) recommended.

Performance Rating

CDX Tasksheet Number: C1003

0	1	2	3	4

Supervisor/instructor signature _____ Date _____

CDX Tasksheet Number: C732

Time off_____

Time on_____

Total time_____

1. Research the following specifications/procedures for this vehicle in the appropriate service information.

   a. Oil pressure specification(s): _____

   b. List or print off and attach to this sheet the procedure for performing the oil pressure test:

2. Using the appropriate tools, remove the oil pressure switch/sensor from the engine block and install the mechanical oil pressure gauge fitting to the place where the switch was fitted. Place the gauge in a position where you can easily view it, but out of the way of any moving parts, exhaust pipes, etc.

3. Prepare to start the vehicle by applying the parking brake and placing exhaust hoses over the exhaust pipe(s).

4. With a relatively cold engine, start the car and note the pressure gauge reading at idle: _____ psi/kPa

5. Increase the engine speed and watch the pressure gauge reading. Note the cold readings below.

   a. @ 1000 rpm: _____ psi/kPa
   b. @ 1500 rpm: _____ psi/kPa
   c. @ 2000 rpm: _____ psi/kPa
   d. @ 2500 rpm: _____ psi/kPa

6. Repeat the readings at a normal engine-operating temperature at idle: _____ psi/kPa. Note the hot readings here.

   a. @ 1000 rpm: _____ psi/kPa
   b. @ 1500 rpm: _____ psi/kPa
   c. @ 2000 rpm: _____ psi/kPa
   d. @ 2500 rpm: _____ psi/kPa

7. Do the readings meet the specifications? Yes: _____ No: _____

8. Determine any necessary action(s):

9. Have your supervisor/instructor verify satisfactory completion of this procedure, any observations found, and any necessary action(s) recommended.

Performance Rating

CDX Tasksheet Number: C732

0	1	2	3	4

Supervisor/instructor signature _____ Date _____

Time off_____

Time on_____

Total time_____

CDX Tasksheet Number: C736

1. Research the following specifications/procedures for this vehicle in the appropriate service information.

   a. Is this vehicle equipped with an oil temperature sensor?
      Yes: _____ No: _____

   b. Is this vehicle equipped with an oil pressure switch (warning light style)?
      Yes: _____ No: _____

   c. Is this vehicle equipped with an oil pressure-sending unit (gauge style)?
      Yes: _____ No: _____

   d. Is the vehicle equipped with an oil pressure sensor (PCM sensor style)?
      Yes: _____ No: _____

   e. List the specification(s) for each sensor/switch the vehicle is equipped with:

      i. Oil temperature sensor:

      ii. Oil pressure switch:

      iii. Oil pressure-sending unit:

      iv. Oil pressure sensor:

2. Following the appropriate service information procedure, test each switch/sensor (as equipped) and list your findings.

   a. Oil temperature sensor:

b. Oil pressure switch:

   c. Oil pressure-sending unit:

   d. Oil pressure sensor:

3. Determine any necessary action(s):

4. Have your supervisor/instructor verify satisfactory completion of this procedure, any observations found, and any necessary action(s) recommended.

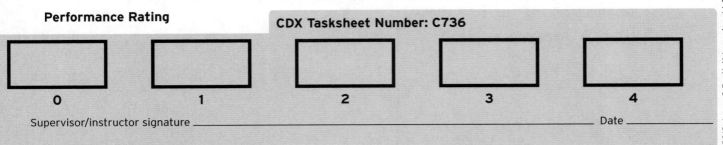

Performance Rating

CDX Tasksheet Number: C736

| 0 | 1 | 2 | 3 | 4 |

Supervisor/instructor signature _____ Date _____

MAST
1D11

CDX Tasksheet Number: C871

1. Research the auxiliary cooler testing procedure for this vehicle in the appropriate service information. Normally, the coolers are located either in front of the radiator or as part of the cooler end of the radiator.

   a. List the auxiliary cooler(s) this vehicle is equipped with (and the type: air-cooled, liquid cooled, etc.):

   b. List or print off and attach to this sheet the inspection and testing procedure for the cooler(s):

2. Closely examine the unit for leaks or damage that could develop into leaks under normal operating conditions. Make particular note of the condition of any tubes or hoses, and the condition of their fittings. List your test(s) and observation(s):

3. Determine any necessary action(s):

4. Return the vehicle to its beginning condition and return any tools that you may have used to their proper locations.

5. Have your supervisor/instructor verify satisfactory completion of this procedure, any observations found, and any necessary action(s) recommended.

Performance Rating

CDX Tasksheet Number: C871

0	1	2	3	4

Supervisor/instructor signature _____ Date _____

Inspect and test coolant; drain and recover coolant; flush and refill cooling system; use proper fluid type per manufacturer specification; bleed air as required.

CDX Tasksheet Number: C050

1. Research the following specifications/procedures for this vehicle in the appropriate service information.

    a. What is the cooling system capacity? _____ qt/lt

    b. What type of antifreeze is required? _____

    c. List or print off and attach to this sheet the cooling system bleeding procedure:

2. Coolant Test:

    a. If the vehicle is cold or cool and not running, remove the radiator cap and test the coolant's freeze protection.

        i. What is the coolant's freeze protection point? _____ °F/°C

    b. List the coolant's boiling point: _____ °F/°C at _____ psi/kPa

    c. Test the coolant's pH reading: _____

        i. Is this within specification? Yes: _____ No: _____

    d. Determine any necessary action(s):

3. Using the appropriate cooling system recycle/flush machine, flush and refill the cooling system with the correct amount of recommended antifreeze. Properly recycle/dispose of any used coolant.

    a. When this procedure is finished, retest the coolant's freeze protection: _____ °F/°C

        i. What is the coolant pH? _____

        ii. Is this within specification? Yes: _____ No: _____

    b. Follow the manufacturer's procedure to bleed air out of the cooling system, if necessary.

    c. Place exhaust hoses on the vehicle's exhaust pipe(s) and wheel chocks to prevent the vehicle from moving. Start the vehicle and monitor the cooling system to make sure that the engine warms up properly and that the thermostat opens at the correct temperature. Also, check that the coolant is at the correct level.

    d. Determine any necessary action(s):

4. **Return the vehicle to its beginning condition and return any tools that you may have used to their proper locations.**

5. **Have your supervisor/instructor verify satisfactory completion of this procedure, any observations found, and any necessary action(s) recommended.**

Performance Rating

CDX Tasksheet Number: C050

0	1	2	3	4

Supervisor/instructor signature _____ Date _____

MAST
1D5

CDX Tasksheet Number: C680

1. **Research the following specifications/procedures for this vehicle in the appropriate service information.**

   a. **Water pump bolt torque:** _____ **ft-lb/N·m**

   b. **Type of antifreeze:** _____

   c. **Draw or print off and attach to this sheet the belt routing diagram:**

2. **Drain the coolant out of the radiator. In most situations, the coolant gets replaced/recycled. If your instructor wants you to reuse the coolant, save it in a clean container and keep it free of dirt and debris.**

3. **Following the specified procedure, remove the water pump.**

4. **Inspect the pump for signs of deterioration, leaks, and worn bearings. List your observations:**

5. **Have your instructor verify the removal of the water pump. Supervisor's/instructor's initials:** _____

6. **Replace the water pump with a new water pump, if needed. Torque all fasteners to the proper torque.**

7. **Reinstall the removed coolant (or new coolant) into the radiator. Top off with the correct coolant, if needed.**

8. **Pressure test or vacuum test the cooling system to check for leaks. Repair any leaks found.**

9. **Apply the vehicle's parking brake or secure the vehicle with wheel chocks to prevent the vehicle from rolling. Also, place the exhaust hose over the exhaust pipe(s).**

10. **Start the vehicle and check for any leaks or overheating. Immediately shut off the vehicle if a leak or overheating is found. Repair any leaks, or determine the reason for overheating if present.**

11. **Return the vehicle to its beginning condition and return any tools that you may have used to their proper locations.**

12. Have your supervisor/instructor verify satisfactory completion of this procedure, any observations found, and any necessary action(s) recommended.

Performance Rating

CDX Tasksheet Number: C680

☐	☐	☐	☐	☐
0	1	2	3	4

Supervisor/instructor signature _____ Date _____

MAST
1D3

Time off_____

Time on_____

Total time_____

CDX Tasksheet Number: C734

1. Locate "inspecting, adjusting and or replacing a generator (alternator) drive belts, pulleys, and tensioners; check pulley and belt alignment" in the appropriate service information for the vehicle you are working on.

    a. List the specified drive belt tension: _____

    b. List the faults to look for when inspecting drive belts, pulleys, and tensioners:

    c. Describe how to check the correct pulley and belt alignment:

    d. Locate the belt routing diagram, or draw a picture of the current routing arrangement:

2. Remove the vehicle drive belt(s).

3. Inspect the vehicle drive belts, pulleys, and tensioners for faults. List your observations for the following parts:

    a. Vehicle drive belt(s):

b. Pulleys:

   c. Tensioner(s):

   d. Pulley/belt alignment:

4. **Have your instructor verify the removal of the belt(s) and the faults found. Supervisor's/instructor's initials:** _____

5. **Reinstall the vehicle drive belts using the appropriate service information.**

6. **Re-tension the drive belt(s) using the appropriate service information.**

7. **Check for the correct pulley, tensioner, and drive belt alignment.**

8. **Determine any necessary action(s):**

9. **Have your supervisor/instructor verify satisfactory completion of this procedure, any observations found, and any necessary action(s) recommended.**

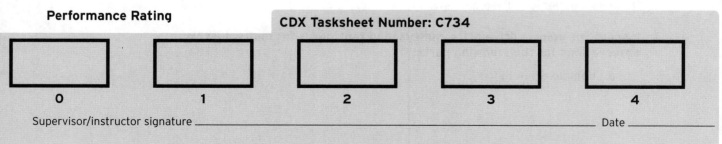

Performance Rating

CDX Tasksheet Number: C734

| 0 | 1 | 2 | 3 | 4 |

Supervisor/instructor signature _____ Date _____

Additional Task

Time off_____

Time on_____

Total time_____

CDX Tasksheet Number: N/A

1. Visually inspect the external condition of all the hoses that carry coolant on the vehicle. Also, squeeze each hose and check for soft or brittle conditions. List your observations below.

   a. Radiator hose condition:

   b. Heater hose condition:

   c. Other hoses (bypass hoses, heated intake hoses, etc.):

2. Drain an appropriate amount of coolant from the system to lower the coolant level below the level of the hose you are removing.

3. Remove the hose. Be careful not to damage the fitting it is connected to.

> **NOTE** Do not twist the hose to loosen it from the radiator or heater core fittings. You could pull the fitting out of the core. Either carefully slide a tool between the fitting and the hose, or slit the hose on top of the fitting, being careful not to damage the fitting, and peel the hose off of the fitting.

4. Inspect the inside of the hose. List your observation(s):

5. Have your instructor verify the removal and the faults found. Supervisor's/instructor's initials: _____

6. Replace the hose with a new one, if needed. Be sure to properly route it.

7. Refill the system with the proper coolant; perform a pressure or vacuum test to check for leaks.

8. Apply the vehicle's parking brake and secure the vehicle with wheel chocks to prevent the vehicle from rolling. Also, place the exhaust hose over the exhaust pipe(s).

9. Start the engine and allow it to warm up to a normal operating temperature and recheck for leaks and proper coolant level.

10. Have your supervisor/instructor verify satisfactory completion of this procedure, any observations found, and any necessary action(s) recommended.

Performance Rating

CDX Tasksheet Number: N/A

0	1	2	3	4

Supervisor/instructor signature _____ Date _____

► TASK Inspect engine cooling and heater system hoses and pipes; perform needed action.

MAST
7C1

Time off_____

Time on_____

Total time_____

CDX Tasksheet Number: C364

Vehicle used for this activity:

Year _____ Make _____ Model _____

Odometer _____ VIN _____

1. **Research the procedure and specifications for inspecting and replacing cooling system hoses and belts in the appropriate service information.**

    a. **Specified change interval for radiator hoses:** _____ **miles/months**

    b. **Specified change interval for heater hoses:** _____ **miles/months**

    c. **Describe what to look for when inspecting cooling system hoses:**

2. **Inspect the cooling and heater system hoses. List your observations:**

3. **Using a cooling system pressure tester, pressurize the cooling system to the specified radiator cap pressure. Inspect the cooling system for leaks. List your observations:**

4. **Have your supervisor/instructor verify your observations. Supervisor's/instructor's initials:** _____

5. **Perform any necessary actions and list your observation(s):**

6. **Have your supervisor/instructor verify satisfactory completion of this procedure, any observations found, and any necessary action(s) recommended.**

Performance Rating

CDX Tasksheet Number: C364

0	1	2	3	4

Supervisor/instructor signature _____ Date _____

▶ TASK Remove, inspect, and replace thermostat and gasket/seal.

CDX Tasksheet Number: C735

Time off_____

Time on_____

Total time_____

1. Research the thermostat replacement procedure for this vehicle in the appropriate service information.

    a. List any special procedures and/or tools to perform this task:

    b. List the thermostat housing bolt torque: _____ ft-lb/N·m

2. Look up the flat rate time for this task in a flat rate manual: _____ hr

3. Drain enough coolant out of the radiator to lower the level below the thermostat. Save this to put back in the system when the task is finished. Keep it free of dirt and debris.

4. Follow the manufacturer's procedure and remove the thermostat.

5. Carefully scrape off any old gasket residue from the thermostat housing and mating surface. Be careful not to gouge the sealing surfaces.

6. Have your instructor verify removal of the thermostat. Supervisor's/instructor's initials: _____

> **NOTE** Ask your supervisor/instructor whether or not to perform the next action before proceeding.

7. Test the old thermostat in a pan of boiling water to see at what temperature it opens. Suspend the thermostat in a pan of heated water using a piece of wire. The thermostat should be fully immersed in water, but do not allow it to touch the side or bottom of the pan.

    a. List the temperature at which the thermostat started to open:
    _____ °F/°C
    b. List the temperature at which the thermostat was fully open:
    _____ °F/°C
    c. How far did the thermostat open? _____ in/mm
    d. Did the thermostat operate according to specifications?
    Yes: _____ No: _____

8. Install a new thermostat and gasket/seal (or reinstall the old one if your instructor directed you to do so). Torque bolts to the proper torque.

> **NOTE** Be careful when bolting down the thermostat housing. Make sure the thermostat is still in its recessed groove. Failure to do so will result in a broken housing and damaged thermostat. If in doubt, ask your supervisor/instructor.

9. Once the thermostat is installed, return the drained antifreeze back into the system.

10. Follow the manufacturer's procedure to bleed any air from the cooling system.

11. Apply the vehicle's parking brake and secure the vehicle with wheel chocks to prevent the vehicle from rolling. Also, place the exhaust hose over the exhaust pipe(s).

12. Start the vehicle and check for any leaks or overheating. Immediately shut off the vehicle if a leak or overheating is found. Repair any leaks, or determine the reason for overheating if present.

13. Return the vehicle to its beginning condition and return any tools that you may have used to their proper locations.

14. Have your supervisor/instructor verify satisfactory completion of this procedure, any observations found, and any necessary action(s) recommended.

Performance Rating

CDX Tasksheet Number: C735

0	1	2	3	4

Supervisor/instructor signature _____ Date _____

CDX Tasksheet Number: C598

Time off_____

Time on_____

Vehicle used for this activity:

Year _____ Make _____ Model_____

Odometer_____ VIN_____

Total time_____

1. **List the customer concern in relation to the overheating problem:**

2. **Research the particular concern in the appropriate service information and list the possible causes:**

3. **Inspect the cooling system and engine to determine the cause of the concern. List your tests and results:**

4. **Determine any necessary action(s) to correct the fault:**

5. **Return the vehicle to its beginning condition and return any tools that you may have used to their proper locations.**

6. **Have your supervisor/instructor verify satisfactory completion of this procedure, any observations found, and any necessary action(s) recommended.**

Performance Rating

CDX Tasksheet Number: C598

0	1	2	3	4

Supervisor/instructor signature _____ Date _____

▶ TASK Perform cooling system pressure and dye tests to identify leaks; check coolant condition; inspect and test radiator, pressure cap, coolant recovery tank, heater core , and galley plugs; determine needed action.

MAST
1D1

Time off_____

Time on_____

Total time_____

CDX Tasksheet Number: C578

1. **Research the following specifications for this vehicle in the appropriate service information.**

    a. **Radiator cap pressure rating:** _____ psi/kPa
    b. **Cooling system capacity:** _____ qt/lt
    c. **Type of coolant:** _____
    d. **Specified pH:** _____

2. **Cooling System Pressure Test: If the vehicle is cold or cool, and the engine is not running, remove the radiator cap. Top off the radiator with the correct type of coolant/water mix if it is not already full. Install the proper adapter on the cooling system access point. Pressurize the cooling system to the specified radiator cap pressure listed above (or a maximum of 2 psi higher). Make sure you leave the system pressurized for a minimum of 10 minutes while you inspect for coolant leaks.**

    > **NOTE** Do not forget to check the heater core and the core plugs.

    a. **List any leaks found and any necessary action(s):**

3. **Coolant Condition: Remove the pressure tester from the radiator. Fit the proper adapter on the tester so that you can check the radiator cap.**

    a. **Pressure-test the cap and check it for the following information.**

        i.   **At what pressure does it vent?** _____ psi/kPa
        ii. **At what pressure does it hold?** _____ psi/kPa
        iii. **Determine any necessary action(s):**

4. **Check Coolant Condition: With the engine cold or cool, and the pressure cap removed, check the condition and level of the coolant.**
    a. **Do a visual inspection of the coolant. List your findings and any necessary action(s).**

    b. **Check the level of the coolant in both the overflow bottle and the radiator. List your findings and any necessary action(s).**

5. **Radiator, Recovery Tank, and Hoses:** Inspect the radiator, recovery tank, and hoses for damage or broken/missing pieces. List your findings and any necessary action(s):

6. **Radiator Test:** Reinstall the radiator cap on the radiator. Place the exhaust hose over the vehicle's exhaust pipe(s). Start the vehicle and allow the engine to warm up.

   a. Use the infrared temperature gun to measure the temperature across the radiator core. The temperature should show a steady cooling reading as you trace the core tubes from the hot side of the radiator to the cool side. Any tubes that are significantly cooler than the others indicate a plugged tube in the radiator.

   b. List your observations and determine any necessary action(s):

7. Have your supervisor/instructor verify satisfactory completion of this procedure, any observations found, and any necessary action(s) recommended.

Performance Rating

CDX Tasksheet Number: C578

0	1	2	3	4

Supervisor/instructor signature _____ Date _____

MAST
8A10

CDX Tasksheet Number: C398

1. Research the following specifications in the service information.

   a. Thermostat opening temperature: _____ °F/°C

   b. Temperature at which the electric fan comes on (if equipped): _____ °F/°C

   c. Temperature at which the fan clutch engages (on) (if equipped): _____ °F/°C

2. Apply the vehicle's parking brake and secure the vehicle with wheel chocks to prevent the vehicle from rolling.

3. Start the vehicle. Allow the vehicle to warm up while monitoring the engine temperature with the temp gun. Find the spot where the highest temperature reading is found on the engine side of the thermostat housing (on most engines). Monitor the temperature at that spot.

> **NOTE** The temperature should rise to between the thermostat opening temperature and the electric (or clutch) fan "on" temperature (if equipped). If this happens, continue to the next step. If the engine doesn't get that hot, diagnose the problem and go to step 4 below. Do NOT allow the engine to overheat!

   a. If the engine is equipped with an electric fan, the temperature should vary between the electric fan "on" temperature and the electric fan "off" temperature. Record these temperatures:

   i. Electric fan "on" temp: _____ °F/°C

   ii. Electric fan "off" temp: _____ °F/°C

   b. If the engine is equipped with a clutch fan, the temperature should rise above the thermostat opening temperature but not above the clutch fan engagement temperature. Record these two temperatures:

   i. Clutch fan "engaged" temp: _____ °F/°C

   ii. Clutch fan "disengaged" temp: _____ °F/°C

   c. If the engine is equipped with a mechanical fan without a clutch, the temperature should rise to, or slightly above, the thermostat opening temperature and should remain fairly steady. Record this operating temperature:

   i. Engine operating temperature: _____ °F/°C

4. If the engine did not reach the specified thermostat opening temperature, list the max temperature reached: _____ °F/°C

5. Determine any necessary action(s):

6. Have your supervisor/instructor verify satisfactory completion of this procedure, any observations found, and any necessary action(s) recommended.

Performance Rating

0	1	2	3	4

Supervisor/instructor signature _____ Date _____

MAST
1D8

Time off_____

Time on_____

Total time_____

CDX Tasksheet Number: C053

Mechanical Fans:

1. Research the fan inspection and testing procedure for this vehicle in the appropriate service information.

    a. List or print off and attach to this sheet the inspection and testing procedure for the fan system:

2. Visually inspect the fan and fan clutch for damage or wear and list your observations:

3. Test the fan clutch according to the specified procedure and list your observations:

4. Determine any necessary action(s):

Electric Fans:

1. Research the fan inspection and testing procedure for this vehicle in the appropriate service information.

    a. List or print off and attach to this sheet the inspection and testing procedure for the fan system:

    b. List the temperature at which the electric fan should turn on: _____ °F/°C

2. **Visually inspect the fan for damage or wear and list your observations:**

3. **Test the fan system according to the specified procedure and list your observations:**

4. **Determine any necessary action(s):**

Fan Shroud and Air Dam:

1. **Visually inspect the fan shroud and air dam for any damage, missing parts, or wear and list your observations:**

2. **Determine any necessary action(s):**

3. **Return the vehicle to its beginning condition and return any tools that you may have used to their proper locations.**

4. **Have your supervisor/instructor verify satisfactory completion of this procedure, any observations found, and any necessary action(s) recommended.**

Performance Rating

CDX Tasksheet Number: CO53

0	1	2	3	4

Supervisor/instructor signature _____ Date _____

Inspect and test heater control valve(s); perform needed action.

MAST
7C2

Time off_____

Time on_____

Total time_____

CDX Tasksheet Number: C370

Vehicle used for this activity:

Year _____ Make _____ Model_____

Odometer_____ VIN_____

1. **Research the procedure and specifications for inspecting and testing the heater control valve(s) in the appropriate service information.**

    a. **Specified type of heater control valve(s): Cable: _____
    Vacuum: _____ Electric: _____**

    b. **What does the temperature adjusting mechanism regulate?
    Coolant:_____ Air: _____**

2. **Following the specified procedure, inspect and test the heater control valve(s). List your tests and observation(s):**

3. **Determine any necessary action(s):**

4. **Have your supervisor/instructor verify satisfactory completion of this procedure, any observations found, and any necessary action(s) recommended.**

Performance Rating

CDX Tasksheet Number: C370

0	1	2	3	4

Supervisor/instructor signature _____ Date _____

Time off_____

Time on_____

Total time_____

CDX Tasksheet Number: CO52

1. Research the following specifications/procedures for this vehicle in the appropriate service information.

   a. Cooling system capacity: _____ qt/lt

   b. Type of antifreeze: _____

2. Drain as much coolant from the vehicle as possible into a clean drain pan so that you can reuse the coolant. Also, place the drain pan so that dirt and other debris will not contaminate it while removing the radiator.

3. Follow the specified procedure to remove the radiator.

   NOTE Be careful when removing the hoses from the radiator. You will need to slide a thin tool (such as a small screwdriver) carefully between the hose and the radiator fitting to loosen the hose, or slit the hose and carefully peel it off of the fitting. Failure to do this could cause damage to the radiator fitting.

4. Inspect the radiator for any damage and list your observation(s):

5. Have your instructor verify the removal of the radiator.
   Supervisor's/instructor's initials: _____

6. Reinstall the radiator following the specified procedure.

7. Reinstall the removed coolant into the radiator. Top off with the correct coolant, if needed.

8. Pressure test or vacuum test the cooling system to check for leaks. Repair any leaks found.

9. Apply the vehicle's parking brake or secure the vehicle with wheel chocks to prevent the vehicle from rolling. Also, place the exhaust hose over the exhaust pipe(s).

10. Start the vehicle and check for any leaks or overheating. Immediately shut off the vehicle if a leak or overheating is found. Repair any leaks, or determine the reason for overheating if present.

11. **Have your supervisor/instructor verify satisfactory completion of this procedure, any observations found, and any necessary action(s) recommended.**

Performance Rating

CDX Tasksheet Number: C052

0	1	2	3	4

Supervisor/instructor signature _____ Date _____

▶ **TASK** Determine procedure to remove, inspect, reinstall, and/or replace heater core.

MAST
7C4

Time off_____

Time on_____

Total time_____

CDX Tasksheet Number: C864

Vehicle used for this activity:

Year _____ Make _____ Model_____

Odometer_____ VIN_____

1. **Research the procedure and specifications for inspecting and replacing the heater core in the appropriate service information.**

    a. **List the flat rate time for removing and replacing the heater core:**
    _____ hr

    b. **Does this task require evacuation of the A/C refrigerant?**
    Yes _____ No _____

    c. **List, or print off and attach to this sheet, the steps to remove and replace the heater core:**

2. **List, or print off and attach to this sheet, the steps to inspect the heater core:**

3. **Have your supervisor/instructor verify satisfactory completion of this procedure, any observations found, and any necessary action(s) recommended.**

Performance Rating

CDX Tasksheet Number: C864

0	1	2	3	4

Supervisor/instructor signature _____ Date _____

Research vehicle service information including vehicle service history, service precautions, and technical service bulletins.

MAST
6A1

Time off_____

Time on_____

Total time_____

CDX Tasksheet Number: C286

1. **Using the VIN for identification, use the appropriate source to access the vehicle's service history in relation to prior electrical system work or customer concerns.**

    a. **List any related repairs/concerns, and their dates:**

2. **Using the VIN for identification, access any relevant technical service bulletins for the particular vehicle you are working on in relation to electrical system updates or other service issues.**

    a. **List any related service bulletins and their titles:**

3. **Research the operation of the headlights.**

    a. **Are they protected by a fuse? Yes: _____ No: _____**
    b. **Are they protected by a circuit breaker? Yes: _____ No: _____**
    c. **Do they use a relay? Yes: _____ No: _____**

4. **Have your supervisor/instructor verify satisfactory completion of this procedure, any observations found, and any necessary action(s) recommended.**

Performance Rating

CDX Tasksheet Number: C286

0	1	2	3	4

Supervisor/instructor signature _____ Date _____

Demonstrate knowledge of the causes and effects from shorts, grounds, opens, and resistance problems in electrical/electronic circuits.

Time off_____

Time on_____

Total time_____

CDX Tasksheet Number: C296

1. Define "short circuit":

2. Define "short to ground":

3. Define "short to power":

4. Define "open circuit":

5. Define "high resistance":

6. List at least two examples of short circuits:

7. List at least two examples of grounded circuits:

8. List at least two examples of open circuits:

9. List at least two examples of high resistance in a circuit:

10. What are the effects of a short circuit in a load?

11. What are the effects on a circuit with an open circuit?

12. What are the effects on a circuit with high resistance?

13. Have your supervisor/instructor verify satisfactory completion of your answers in steps 1–12.

© 2019 Jones & Bartlett Learning, LLC, an Ascend Learning Company

Performance Rating

CDX Tasksheet Number: C296

0	1	2	3	4

Supervisor/instructor signature _____ Date _____

MAST
6A2

CDX Tasksheet Number: C951

> **NOTE** Use Ohm's Law to solve the circuit information in this task.

1. **Series Circuit: Circuit voltage = 12 volts, R1 = 3 ohms, R2 = 9 ohms**

    a. **Draw this circuit in the space below:**

    b. **Total circuit resistance:** _____ **ohms**
    c. **Total circuit current flow:** _____ **amps**
    d. **Voltage drop across R1:** _____ **volts**
    e. **Voltage drop across R2:** _____ **volts**
    f. **Current flow through R1:** _____ **amps**
    g. **Current flow through R2:** _____ **amps**

2. **Parallel Circuit: Circuit voltage = 12 volts and Branch 1, R1 = 2 ohms and Branch 2, R2 = 4 ohms**

    a. **Draw this circuit in the space below:**

    b. **Total circuit resistance:** _____ **ohms**
        (Hint: Rt = R1 x R2/R1 + R2)
    c. **Total circuit current flow:** _____ **amps**
    d. **Voltage drop across R1:** _____ **volts**
    e. **Voltage drop across R2:** _____ **volts**
    f. **Current flow through R1:** _____ **amps**
    g. **Current flow through R2:** _____ **amps**

3. **Series-Parallel Circuit: Circuit voltage = 12 volts, R1 = 2 ohms is in series with the parallel circuit of R2 = 3 ohms and R3 = 3 ohms**

    a. **Draw this circuit in the space below:**

    b. **Total resistance of the parallel circuit:** _____ **ohms**
    c. **Total circuit resistance:** _____ **ohms**
    d. **Total circuit current flow:** _____ **amps**
    e. **Voltage drop across R1:** _____ **volts**
    f. **Voltage drop across R2 and R3:** _____ **volts**

g. Current flow through R2: _____ amps

h. Current flow through R3: _____ amps

4. Have your supervisor/instructor verify satisfactory completion of this procedure, any observations found, and any necessary action(s) recommended.

Performance Rating

CDX Tasksheet Number: C951

0	1	2	3	4

Supervisor/instructor signature _____ Date _____

Demonstrate the use of the three Cs (concern, cause, and correction).

Time off_____

Time on_____

Total time_____

CDX Tasksheet Number: N/A

1. **Using the following scenario, write up the three Cs as listed on most repair orders. Assume that the customer authorized the recommended repairs.**

   A vehicle is brought to your shop with an electrical concern. The customer tells you that the battery has been going dead for the last few days, but jump starting it would allow him to drive the vehicle. He also said he replaced the battery with a new one, but that didn't solve the problem. You inspect the vehicle and find the following:

   a. The alternator puts out less than half of the current flow at which it is rated. A check of the diodes show shorted diodes, causing a key-off battery drain.
   b. The battery appears to be new and, once charged, passes the capacity test.
   c. The serpentine drive belt appears old, glazed, and excessively cracked.
   d. The starter draw test shows that the starter is drawing the specified amperage; it sounds normal when cranking the engine.
   e. The right front low beam headlamp is burned out.
   f. The battery hold-down is missing.

   > **NOTE** Ask your instructor whether you should use a copy of the shop repair order or the three Cs below to record this information.

2. **Concern/complaint:**

3. **Cause:**

4. **Correction:**

5. **Other recommended service:**

6. **Have your supervisor/instructor verify satisfactory completion of this procedure, any observations found, and any necessary action(s) recommended.**

Performance Rating

CDX Tasksheet Number: N/A

0	1	2	3	4

Supervisor/instructor signature _____ Date _____

▶ TASK Use wiring diagrams during the diagnosis (troubleshooting) of electrical/electronic circuit problems.

MAST
6A7

CDX Tasksheet Number: C952

Time off_____

Time on_____

Total time_____

> **NOTE** This task requires diagnosis of an electrical problem. Please ask your instructor/supervisor to assign you a vehicle that qualifies for this task and several that follow.

1. List the customer concern/complaint:

2. Which electrical circuit(s) are involved?

3. How many circuit protection devices are there in this circuit? _____

   a. List the circuit protection devices in this circuit:

   b. List the circuit control devices in this circuit:

   c. Which side of the load(s) is controlled?

4. Diagnose the fault and list each test and its result:

5. Determine any necessary actions:

6. Have your supervisor/instructor verify satisfactory completion of this procedure, any observations found, and any necessary action(s) recommended.

Performance Rating

CDX Tasksheet Number: C952

0	1	2	3	4

Supervisor/instructor signature _____ Date _____

Inspect, test, repair, and/or replace components, connectors, terminals, harnesses, and wiring in electrical/electronic systems (including solder repairs); determine needed action.

MAST 6A10

Time off_____

Time on_____

Total time_____

CDX Tasksheet Number: C299

Vehicle used for this activity:

Year _____ Make _____ Model_____

Odometer_____ VIN_____

1. **Ask your instructor which of the items listed above you should inspect and test. List here:** _____

    If needed locate the wiring diagram for the component that you are testing. Determine the purpose and operation of the suspected component. (Understanding how a component is designed to operate within a circuit will make it easier to diagnose.)

2. **After inspection and testing of the item, list the needed repair:**

3. **Using the appropriate service information, determine the manufacturer's recommended procedure to complete the needed repair.**

4. **Have your instructor verify the repair procedure. Supervisor's/instructor's initials:** _____

5. **Carry out the suggested repair or replacement procedure. List your tests and results:**

6. **Determine any needed action(s):**

7. Have your supervisor/instructor verify satisfactory completion of this procedure, any observations found, and any needed action(s) recommended.

Performance Rating

0	1	2	3	4

Supervisor/instructor signature _____ Date _____

MAST
6A12

CDX Tasksheet Number: C955

1. Ask your instructor to assign a data bus wiring harness for you to perform this task on.

2. Research the proper steps to repair the data bus wiring harness in the appropriate service information.

    a. List the steps to properly repair the data bus wiring:

3. With your instructor's permission, cut one wire of the data bus system.

    a. Have your instructor verify the cut wire and repair procedure. Supervisor's/instructor's initials: _____

4. Perform the repair; be careful to follow all of the steps of the specified procedure.

5. What did you do to prevent electrical noise from affecting the repaired wires once they are back in service?

6. How did you insulate the soldered joint? _____

7. Have your supervisor/instructor verify satisfactory completion of this procedure, any observations found, and any necessary action(s) recommended.

Performance Rating

CDX Tasksheet Number: C955

0	1	2	3	4

Supervisor/instructor signature _____ Date _____

► **TASK** Demonstrate proper use of a digital multimeter (DMM) when measuring source voltage, voltage drop (including grounds), current flow, and resistance.

MAST
6A3

Time off_____

Time on_____

Total time_____

CDX Tasksheet Number: C641

NOTE This task is best performed on either the CDX DVOM simulator, a physical simulator, or a bugged vehicle.

1. **Ask your instructor what lighting circuit he/she would like you to perform the following meter readings on. List circuit here:**

2. **Using the appropriate wiring diagram as a reference and a DMM, determine the following:**

    a. **Measured source voltage (at battery):** _____ **volts**
    b. **Measured voltage drop (positive side of circuit):** _____ **volts**
    c. **Measured voltage drop (negative side of circuit):** _____ **volts**
    d. **Measured resistance of light:** _____ **ohms**
    e. **Measured current flow through light:** _____ **amps**

3. **Were any of the readings out of specification? Yes:** _____ **No:** _____

    a. **List your observations:**

4. **Have your supervisor/instructor verify satisfactory completion of this procedure and any observations found.**

Performance Rating

CDX Tasksheet Number: C641

0	1	2	3	4

Supervisor/instructor signature _____ Date _____

MAST
6A5

Time off_____

Time on_____

Total time_____

CDX Tasksheet Number: C291

1. **Test for proper operation of the test light by connecting it across the vehicle's battery terminals.**

   a. **Connect the clip end (negative) of the test light to the negative battery terminal.**

   b. **Touch the probe end of the test light to the positive battery terminal. The test light should light.**

   c. **Did the test light operate correctly? Yes: _____ No: _____**

   > **NOTE** Please notify your supervisor/instructor if the test light did not operate correctly.

2. **Using the wiring diagram for the left tail lamp/parking light circuit of the assigned vehicle, identify the wire color for both the power (voltage) and ground (negative) wire.**

   i. **Power (positive):** _____

   ii. **Ground (negative):** _____

3. **Using the appropriate tools, remove the taillight assembly and disconnect the tail lamp connector. The headlamp switch should be set to "Off."**

   a. **Visually locate the power and ground wires, as described in step 2.**

   b. **Turn the headlamp switch to the "Park" position.**

   c. **Connect the clip end of the test light to an unpainted metal surface that is a good ground.**

   d. **Touch the test light probe to the positive wire of the vehicle harness tail lamp connector cavity.**

   i. **Did the test light come on? Yes: _____ No: _____**

   ii. **Please explain your results:**

   e. **With the test light probe still connected to the positive wire, test the ground wire by removing the clip end of the test light and touching it to the ground wire of the tail lamp connector cavity, being careful not to cause a short circuit by touching the clip to the probe. The light should come on if there is a good ground.**

   i. **Did the light come on? Yes: _____ No: _____**

3. **Based on your observations, determine any necessary action(s):**

4. Have your supervisor/instructor verify satisfactory completion of this procedure, any observations found, and any necessary action(s) recommended.

Performance Rating

CDX Tasksheet Number: C291

0	1	2	3	4

Supervisor/instructor signature _____ Date _____

MAST
6A6

CDX Tasksheet Number: C295

Time off_____

Time on_____

Total time_____

> **NOTE** Using a jumper wire to bypass components can cause damage if performed incorrectly. Never bypass the load in any circuit. Normally it is acceptable to bypass switches and some speed controlling resistors. If in doubt, ask your instructor.

1. Ask your instructor to assign you a vehicle equipped with an electric cooling fan controlled by a relay.

2. Research the wiring diagram for the cooling fan circuit. Draw a diagram of that circuit.

3. Locate the cooling fan relay.

4. Draw a diagram of the relay socket and label each terminal with where the wire comes from, or goes to.

5. Label the diagram with the two points to which you believe the jumper wires should be placed.

6. Apply the parking brake and make sure the vehicle is in park or neutral.

7. Ask your instructor to verify your answers and where you plan to place the fused jumper wire. Have him/her watch you during the next portion of this task to ensure no damage is done to the vehicle's electrical system.

   a. Supervisor's/instructor's initials: _____

8. Turn the ignition switch to the run position, but do not start the vehicle (Key On, Engine Off - KOEO).

9. Use the fused jumper wire to activate the relay by jumping the terminals that connect to the relay contacts.

   a. List your observation(s):

10. Determine any necessary action(s):

11. Have your supervisor/instructor verify satisfactory completion of this procedure, any observations found, and any necessary action(s) recommended.

Performance Rating

CDX Tasksheet Number: C295

0	1	2	3	4

Supervisor/instructor signature _____ Date _____

Inspect and test fusible links, circuit breakers, and fuses; determine needed action.

Time off_____

Time on_____

Total time_____

CDX Tasksheet Number: C298

1. Using the appropriate service information, locate the fuse panel(s) for the vehicle/simulator you are assigned to.

    a. List the locations of the fuse panel(s) and circuit protection devices for this vehicle/simulator:

2. Use a test light to test each fuse and circuit breaker in one of the fuse boxes. List any circuit protection devices that are defective (open).

NOTE Circuit protection devices normally do not wear out. If a circuit protection device is found to be faulty, too much current was/is present. You should determine the reason for the fault.

3. What is the rating (size) of the failed circuit protection device?
   _____ amps

4. Is the correct size fuse installed? Yes: _____ No: _____

5. Determine the cause for the circuit protection device to fail. List your tests and results below.

6. Determine any necessary action(s):

7. Have your supervisor/instructor verify satisfactory completion of this procedure, any observations found, and any necessary action(s) recommended.

Performance Rating

0	1	2	3	4

Supervisor/instructor signature _____ Date _____

Inspect and test switches, connectors, and wires of
starter control circuits; determine needed action.

MAST
6C5

CDX Tasksheet Number: C313

1. Refering to the appropriate service information, draw a diagram of the starter control circuit (small wires) from battery positive terminal to the starter. On the diagram, list the components the current goes through to get to the starter.

   a. List the maximum specified voltage drop across the starter relay/solenoid contacts: _____ volts

2. Write a short description of how the starter control circuit operates to enable the starter to crank the engine:

3. Disable the vehicle's fuel or ignition system so it will not start.

4. Conduct the Starter Control Circuit Voltage Drop Test–Positive Side.

   a. List the voltmeter connection points in the circuit:

   DMM black lead: _____

   DMM red lead: _____

   b. Conduct the Starter Control Circuit Voltage Drop Test:

   What is the voltage drop on the positive side? _____ volts

   Is this reading within specifications? Yes: _____ No: _____

   i. If no, refer to the service information for further tests. List those tests and their results:

5. Determine any necessary action(s):

6. Have your supervisor/instructor verify satisfactory completion of this procedure, any observations found, and any necessary action(s) recommended.

Performance Rating

0	1	2	3	4

Supervisor/instructor signature _____ Date _____

▶ TASK Check electrical/electronic circuit waveforms; interpret
readings and determine needed repairs.

MAST
6A11

Time off_____

Time on_____

Total time_____

CDX Tasksheet Number: C642

Vehicle used for this activity:

Year _____ Make _____ Model_____

Odometer_____ VIN_____

1. **List the two most common types of electrical waveforms and describe how each of them differ:**

2. **Research various sensors for the vehicle you have been given.**

   a. **List at least two sensors that give an analog signal:**

   b. **List at least two sensors that give a digital signal:**

3. **Connect a lab scope to at least one analog sensor. Test the sensor, draw a diagram of the waveform, and list the name of the analog sensor:**

4. **Connect a lab scope to at least one digital sensor. Test the sensor, draw a diagram of the waveform, and list the name of the digital sensor:**

5. **Do these waveforms meet the manufacturer's specifications?**
   Yes: _____ No: _____

6. Determine any necessary action(s):

7. Have your supervisor/instructor verify satisfactory completion of this procedure, any observations found, and any necessary action(s) recommended.

Performance Rating

CDX Tasksheet Number: C642

0	1	2	3	4

Supervisor/instructor signature _____ Date _____

CDX Tasksheet Number: C819

> **NOTE** Recharging a battery differs from manufacturer to manufacturer. It is important that you follow the recharging steps recommended by the manufacturer of the battery that is assigned to you.

1. **Research slow and/or fast battery charging for this vehicle battery in the appropriate service information. Follow all directions. If no directions are given, use the following information:**

    It is best to disconnect the negative battery terminal when charging a battery. Consider using a memory minder to maintain the memories on electronic control modules.

    The ideal rate for charging a battery can be found by dividing the battery's CCA by 70.

    To find the maximum charging rate for fast charging a battery, divide the battery's CCA by 40.

    The faster a battery is charged, the shorter its life.

    Do not exceed: 15.5V on a flooded cell battery; 14.8V on an AGM battery; or 14.3V on a gel cell battery.

2. **List the steps for recharging this battery:**

3. **What method is recommended for recharging the battery?**
    Slow charge: _____ Fast charge: _____

    a. **Have your supervisor/instructor verify the steps above. Supervisor's/ instructor's initials: _____**

4. **Charge the battery according to the manufacturer's recommendations.**
    a. **How long did the battery charge? _____ time**
    b. **What was the highest amperage reading during charging? _____ amps**
    c. **What was the lowest amperage reading during charging? _____ amps**
    d. **What was the highest voltage during charging? _____ volts**
    e. **How did you determine the battery was fully charged?**

5. **Determine any necessary action(s):**

6. Have your supervisor/instructor verify satisfactory completion of this procedure, any observations found, and any necessary action(s) recommended.

Performance Rating

CDX Tasksheet Number: C819

0	1	2	3	4

Supervisor/instructor signature _____ Date _____

Jump-start vehicle using jumper cables and a booster battery or an auxiliary power supply.

MAST
6B6

Time off_____

Time on_____

Total time_____

CDX Tasksheet Number: C820

1. Research "starting a vehicle with a dead battery" or "jump starting procedures" in the appropriate service information for the vehicle you are working on. List the steps as outlined in the service information.

> **NOTE** Caution: Some vehicle manufacturers prohibit jump-starting of their vehicles. If this is the case, inform your supervisor/instructor.

> **NOTE** Follow these steps exactly!

2. Why is the last connection away from the battery, preferably on an unpainted solid metal component connected to the engine block?

3. Have your supervisor/instructor verify your answers. Supervisor's/instructor's initials: _____

4. Connect the jumper cables as outlined in the service information or connect the auxiliary power supply (jump box) as was outlined in the service information.

5. Start the engine.

6. Remove the cables in the reverse order as they were installed.

7. Have your supervisor/instructor verify satisfactory completion of this procedure, any observations found, and any necessary action(s) recommended.

Performance Rating

CDX Tasksheet Number: C820

0	1	2	3	4

Supervisor/instructor signature _____ Date _____

Inspect and clean battery; fill battery cells; check battery cables, connectors, clamps, and hold-downs.

MAST
6B4

Time off_____

Time on_____

Total time_____

CDX Tasksheet Number: C644

1. **On the vehicle that was assigned to you by your supervisor/instructor, and following all steps listed in the service information, disconnect the negative battery terminal and move it out of the way so it cannot touch the terminal, or spring back against it. (Consider using a memory minder.)**

2. **Disconnect the positive battery terminal and move it out of the way. Place a glove or other insulating material over the end of the battery cable to prevent shorting out the memory minder.**

3. **Remove the battery hold-down so that the battery is sitting in the battery tray or box.**

4. **Remove the battery from the battery tray.**

5. **Inspect the battery hold-down hardware and the battery tray. List your observations:**

6. **Clean the battery, battery terminals, battery tray, and hold-down hardware with a suitable cleaner or by mixing baking soda and water.**

> NOTE The consistency of the baking soda and water should be like a thin paste. The use of a small brush will help the cleaning process.

7. **Rinse the components with lots of clean water. Wipe the components dry with some paper towels.**

> NOTE DO NOT USE COMPRESSED AIR! It can blow acid around.

8. **Clean the battery terminals and posts with a battery terminal cleaner.**

9. **Check the battery electrolyte level. This can be done only on non-maintenance-free batteries. If the level is low, add only distilled water to the proper level.**

   a. **Have your supervisor/instructor check your work. Supervisor's/instructor's initials:** _____

10. **Install the battery and hold-down hardware, and reconnect the cables as outlined in the service information.**

11. **Install a battery terminal protective spray onto the battery terminals.**

12. **Determine any necessary action(s):**

13. Have your supervisor/instructor verify satisfactory completion of this procedure, any observations found, and any necessary action(s) recommended.

Performance Rating

CDX Tasksheet Number: C644

0	1	2	3	4

Supervisor/instructor signature _____ Date _____

► **TASK** Perform battery state-of-charge test; determine needed action.

MAST
6B1

CDX Tasksheet Number: C302

1. Research the following specifications for this vehicle in the appropriate service information.

   a. Specified battery capacity: _____ cold cranking amps (CCA)

   b. Group size, if specified: _____ BCI group

   > **NOTE** Check with your supervisor/instructor which of the following tests you are to perform, or whether you should perform all of them.

2. Perform a Specific Gravity Test. The battery must have removable vent caps.

   a. Locate and review the "Specific Gravity State of Charge Test" in the appropriate service information.

   b. Clean the top of the battery.

   > **NOTE** This must be done prior to the removal of the vent caps.

   c. Remove the vent caps.

   d. Verify that the electrolyte level is high enough above the cells to fill the hydrometer.

   e. Draw enough electrolyte from a cell so the float is suspended. Determine the specific gravity reading and return the electrolyte into the cell. Repeat this for each cell and record your readings below. Be sure to compensate for temperature if you are using a hydrometer that is not automatically temperature compensated.

   Cell #1: _____

   Cell #2: _____

   Cell #3: _____

   Cell #4: _____

   Cell #5: _____

   Cell #6: _____

   f. Calculate the maximum difference between the cell readings: _____

   g. What is the maximum allowable difference in cell readings: _____

   h. Compare the readings to the information in the service information, and list the state of charge: _____ %

   i. Clean the hydrometer and tools.

3. Perform an Open Circuit Voltage Test. This test is for maintenance-free or non-vented batteries.

   a. Locate and review the "Open Circuit Voltage Test" in the service Information.

   b. Make sure the engine is off and the battery is stabilized. If the battery has just been recharged, you must remove the surface charge. Wait at least 5 minutes after removing the surface charge before measuring the open circuit voltage. Please follow the manufacturer's recommendations closely.

c. Prepare the digital multimeter (DMM) to measure voltage.

d. Place the red lead on the positive post/terminal and the black lead on the negative post/terminal.

e. What is the measured voltage (open-circuit voltage) of the battery? _____ volts

f. The table below represents the open-circuit voltage of the battery. Please select the battery's percent of charge as it relates to the voltage measured.

Voltage	Percent Charge
12.6 or greater	100
12.4–12.6	75–100
12.2–12.4	50–75
12.0–12.2	25–50
11.7–12.0	0–25
0.0–11.7	0; no charge

4. **Perform a Conductance Test.**

a. Review the process for performing a battery conductance test.

b. Connect the conductance tester to the battery terminals (some testers require the removal of the battery cable for accuracy).

c. Follow the prompts on the conductance tester for the type and CCAs of the battery being tested.

d. Start the conductance test.

e. List the state of charge (usually a % of charge): _____ %

f. Record the available CCAs listed on the conductance tester: _____

5. **Determine any necessary action(s):**

6. **Have your supervisor/instructor verify satisfactory completion of this procedure, any observations found, and any necessary action(s) recommended.**

Performance Rating

CDX Tasksheet Number: C302

| 0 | 1 | 2 | 3 | 4 |

Supervisor/instructor signature _____ Date _____

© 2019 Jones & Bartlett Learning, LLC, an Ascend Learning Company

► **TASK** Confirm proper battery capacity for vehicle application; perform battery capacity and load test; determine needed action.

CDX Tasksheet Number: C818

Time off_____

Time on_____

Total time_____

> **NOTE** The battery capacity test is also known as a load test or battery performance test. Follow all directions of the manufacturer whose tool you are using to load test the battery.

1. Research the specifications and procedures for testing the battery in the appropriate service information.

   a. What is the specified battery capacity for the vehicle you are working on?
   _____ CCA

   b. What type of battery is specified for this battery?
   Flooded cell: _____ AGM: _____ Other (list): _____

2. Inspect the battery and find its listed capacity rating: _____

3. Does this battery meet the specified CCA requirements for this vehicle?
   Yes: _____ No: _____

4. Determine the following load test variables for this battery:

   a. Required load test amps: _____ amps

   b. Required load test time (some testers are automatic):
   _____ seconds

5. Connect the load tester as directed by the equipment manufacturer. Make sure the tester clamps are secure on the battery terminals, and the inductive amps clamp is around the proper cable.

6. Load-test the battery. What was the battery minimum voltage (at the end of the load test time)? _____ volts

7. Did the battery pass the load test? Yes: _____ No: _____

8. If a battery fails the load test, what should be done next?

9. Determine any necessary action(s):

10. **Have your supervisor/instructor verify satisfactory completion of this procedure, any observations found, and any necessary action(s) recommended.**

Performance Rating

CDX Tasksheet Number: C818

0	1	2	3	4

Supervisor/instructor signature _____ Date _____

Identify electrical/electronic modules, security systems, radios, and other accessories that require reinitialization or code entry after reconnecting the vehicle battery.

MAST
6B8

CDX Tasksheet Number: C645

1. **Research the components that require reinitialization or code entry on the vehicle you are working on after reconnecting the battery. List those components here:**

2. **List the correct process for reinitialization or code entry for each of the components listed above:**

3. **Have your supervisor/instructor verify satisfactory completion of this procedure, any observations found, and any necessary action(s) recommended.**

Performance Rating

CDX Tasksheet Number: C645

0	1	2	3	4

Supervisor/instructor signature _____ Date _____

MAST
6B3

CDX Tasksheet Number: C304

1. **Research the maintaining or restoring of electronic memory functions for this vehicle in the appropriate service information. Please follow all directions, and note that some vehicle electronic devices REQUIRE specific codes for reinitialization. If you don't have those codes available, do NOT disconnect the battery.**

> **NOTE** Some manufacturers require the use of tools that help maintain memories, such as radios, adaptive strategies, etc. The use of these tools can minimize down time in restoring electronic memories lost when a battery is disconnected. In some cases, the use of a "memory minder," which is basically a battery that plugs into the 12V accessory socket or the data link connector, can be utilized. In all cases, follow the manufacturer's instructions.

2. **Restore electronic memory functions.**

   a. **Change the vehicle's radio pre-set frequencies of the FM (1) stations and list those resets here:**
      1. _____ 2. _____ 3. _____ 4. _____

   b. **With NO memory minder installed, disconnect the negative battery terminal for at least 15 seconds.**

   c. **Reconnect the negative battery terminal, and tighten properly.**

   d. **Check the radio pre-sets. Did they change? Yes: _____ No: _____**

      i. **Why or why not?**

   e. **Restore the frequencies, as per manufacturer recommendations, to the stations noted in step 2a.**

   f. **What would you have to do to restore the vehicle's PCM adaptive learning memory if it is erased?**

3. **Maintain the electronic memory functions**

   a. **Reset the radio pre-sets to the same stations you did before.**

   b. **Install a memory minder to maintain electrical power in the system.**

   c. **Disconnect the negative battery terminal for at least 1 minute.**

   d. **Check the radio pre-sets. Did they change? Yes: _____ No: _____**

      i. **Why or why not?**

e. Under this scenario, what happens to the vehicle's PCM adaptive learning memory if the battery is disconnected?

4. What did you learn?

5. Have your supervisor/instructor verify satisfactory completion of this procedure, any observations found, and any necessary action(s) recommended.

Performance Rating

CDX Tasksheet Number: C304

0	1	2	3	4

Supervisor/instructor signature _____ Date _____

Diagnose the cause(s) of excessive key-off battery drain
(parasitic draw); determine needed action.

MAST
6A8

CDX Tasksheet Number: C817

> **NOTE** Be sure to follow the correct steps for connecting your DMM to check for amperage/current flow. Have your supervisor/instructor check your connections. Improper connection of the DMM may damage your meter.

1. **Research key-off battery drain (parasitic drain) checks in the appropriate service information.**

    a. **List the maximum allowable key-off battery drain (parasitic drain) for the vehicle/simulator that has been assigned to you. What is the maximum allowable drain? _____ mA**

    b. **What is the specified time for the last module to go to sleep? _____ sec/min**

2. **List the appropriate steps to measure the key-off battery drain (parasitic drain):**

3. **Using the steps listed, measure the key off battery drain (parasitic drain):**

    a. **What is the actual drain? _____ mA**

    b. **Is this reading within specifications? Yes: _____ No: _____**

        i. **If no, identify the faulty circuit by pulling and replacing fuses one at a time. Watch the amps reading on the meter to see if it drops. If it drops substantially, you will want to investigate that circuit further, by disconnecting the loads and tracing the wires.**

4. **If pulling the fuses does not identify the faulty circuit, disconnect unfused wires one at a time, such as the alternator output wire and the ignition switch feed wire.**

5. **List the steps you took to diagnose the cause of the parasitic draw and their results:**

6. **Determine any necessary action(s):**

7. What would the customer concern be that would require you to perform this test?

8. Have your supervisor/instructor verify satisfactory completion of this procedure, any observations found, and any necessary action(s) recommended.

Performance Rating

CDX Tasksheet Number: C817

0	1	2	3	4

Supervisor/instructor signature _____ Date _____

CDX Tasksheet Number: N/A

1. Determine what the impedance of the DMM is. List the impedance:
   _____ megohms (meter impedance)

2. Set the DMM to ohms and touch the leads together. This is the delta reading.
   List the reading: _____ ohms (Delta)

   Note: if the meter has a delta adjustment feature, press it so that the meter
   reads 0 ohms when the leads are touching. You won't have to worry about the
   delta reading in this case.

3. With the car off, and all doors closed, wait 30 seconds and then place the
   ohmmeter's black lead on the negative battery terminal and the red lead on the
   alternator case.

4. Read the ohmmeter and subtract the delta reading given previously. List the
   reading: _____ ohms (minus delta reading)

5. Compare this reading to the Chesney Parasitic Load Test graph. Approximately
   how many amps are draining? _____ mA

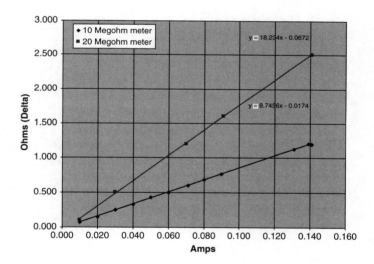

6. Is the reading within specifications?
   Yes: _____ No: _____

7. Open the driver's door and insure at least one dome light is on.

8. Place the black ohmmeter lead on the battery negative and the red lead on the
   alternator case.

9. Read the ohmmeter and subtract the delta reading given previously. List the reading: _____ ohms (minus delta reading)

10. Compare this reading to the Chesney Parasitic Load Test graph. Approximately how many amps are draining? _____ mA

11. Have your supervisor/instructor verify satisfactory completion of this procedure, any observations found, and any necessary action(s) recommended

Performance Rating

CDX Tasksheet Number: N/A

0	1	2	3	4

Supervisor/instructor signature _____ Date _____

▶ **TASK** Demonstrate knowledge of an automatic idle-stop/start-stop system.

MAST
6C7

Time off_____

Time on_____

Total time_____

CDX Tasksheet Number: C1002

1. **Research the description and operation of the automatic idle-stop/start-stop system. Describe in your own words how the automatic idle-stop/start-stop system operates:**

2. **Briefly describe the purpose of the automatic idle-stop/start-stop system:**

3. **Write a short description of the different types of idle-stop/start-stop systems used:**

4. **Have your supervisor/instructor verify satisfactory completion of your answers in steps 1-3.**

Performance Rating

CDX Tasksheet Number: C1002

0	1	2	3	4

Supervisor/instructor signature _____ Date _____

CDX Tasksheet Number: C309

1. Research the specifications and procedures for performing starting system tests and repairs.

   a. List the starter current draw specs: _____ amps at _____ volts (if listed)

2. Connect the starting system tester as outlined in the appropriate service information.

3. This test will require either the fuel system or ignition system to be disabled. Please follow the manufacturer's recommendations for disabling one of these two systems.

4. Identify below which system was disabled and the steps you took to do this:

5. Have your supervisor/instructor check your connections and how you disabled the fuel or ignition system(s).

   a. Supervisor's/instructor's initials: _____

6. Conduct the Starter Current Draw Test.

   a. What was the current draw during the first second or two? _____ amps
   b. What was the final current draw (after three or four seconds)? _____ amps
   c. What was the lowest voltage during the test? _____ volts

7. Compare your results to the manufacturer's specifications. List your observations:

8. Determine any necessary action(s):

9. Have your supervisor/instructor verify satisfactory completion of this procedure, any observations found, and any necessary action(s) recommended.

Performance Rating

CDX Tasksheet Number: C309

0	1	2	3	4

Supervisor/instructor signature _____ Date _____

► **TASK** Perform starter circuit voltage drop tests; determine needed action.

MAST
6C2

CDX Tasksheet Number: C310

1. Research the specifications and procedures for performing the starter circuit voltage drop tests in the appropriate service informaation.

   a. What is the maximum starter circuit (high current cables) voltage drop specification(s) for this test?

      i. Positive side: _____ volts

      ii. Negative (ground) side, if specified: _____ volts

2. Disable the vehicle's fuel or ignition system so it will not start.

3. Conduct the Starter Circuit Voltage Drop Test–Positive/Feed Side (heavy positive battery cable, not the control circuit).

   a. List the voltmeter connection points in the circuit:

      DMM black lead: _____

      DMM red lead: _____

   b. Conduct the Starter Circuit Voltage Drop Test:

      What is the voltage drop on the positive side? _____ volts

      Is this reading within specifications? Yes: _____ No: _____

4. Conduct the Starter Circuit Voltage Drop Test–Ground Side.

   a. List the voltmeter connection points in the circuit:

      DMM black lead: _____

      DMM red lead: _____

   b. Conduct the Starter Circuit Voltage Drop Test:

      What is the voltage drop on the negative side? _____ volts

      Is this reading within specifications? Yes: _____ No: _____

5. Determine any necessary action(s):

6. Have your supervisor/instructor verify satisfactory completion of this procedure, any observations found, and any necessary action(s) recommended.

Performance Rating

CDX Tasksheet Number: C310

| 0 | 1 | 2 | 3 | 4 |

Supervisor/instructor signature _____ Date _____

MAST
6C3

Time off_____

Time on_____

Total time_____

CDX Tasksheet Number: C311

1. Research the procedure and specifications for testing starter relays and solenoids in the appropriate service information.

    a. What is this vehicle's starting system equipped with?
        Starter Solenoid _____ ; Starter Relay _____ ; Both _____
    b. List the resistance of the starter solenoid windings: Pull in: _____ ohms; hold in: _____ ohms
    c. List the specified resistance of the starter relay winding: _____ ohms

2. Disable the vehicle's fuel or ignition system so it will not start.

3. Following the manufacturer's test procedure, list the voltmeter connection points in the circuit to test the voltage drop across the relay or solenoid contacts.

    a. DMM red lead: _____
    b. DMM black lead: _____

4. Conduct the Starter Relay/Solenoid Voltage Drop Test.

    a. List the voltage drop: _____ volts
    b. Is this reading within specifications? Yes: _____ No: _____

5. Measure the resistance of the starter solenoid windings:

    a. Pull in: _____ ohms
    b. Hold in: _____ ohms

6. Measure the resistance of the starter relay winding: _____ ohms

7. Determine any necessary actions:

8. Have your supervisor/instructor verify satisfactory completion of this procedure, any observations found, and any necessary action(s) recommended.

© 2019 Jones & Bartlett Learning, LLC, an Ascend Learning Company

Performance Rating

CDX Tasksheet Number: C311

0	1	2	3	4

Supervisor/instructor signature _____ Date _____

► **TASK** Differentiate between electrical and engine mechanical problems that cause a slow-crank or no-crank condition.

MAST 6C6

Time off_____

Time on_____

Total time_____

CDX Tasksheet Number: C314

Vehicle used for this activity:

Year _____ Make _____ Model_____

Odometer_____ VIN_____

1. **Locate a no-crank or slow-crank starting system symptom chart in the appropriate service information for the vehicle you are working on.**

   a. **Research the repair procedures for the condition of the vehicle, as outlined in the service information, for the vehicle assigned to you.**

2. **Most vehicles can be tested using the following procedure to determine whether the vehicle is experiencing an electrical or mechanical problem: Turn on the headlights and try to start the engine while listening to the starter and watching the headlights. Place a check mark next to the condition below that happened during this test.**

   a. **No starter noises and the headlights stayed at the same intensity:** _____

   > **NOTE** This fault is likely an electrical fault in the starter itself or the control circuit to the starter.

   b. **Loud single click when the key is turned to "crank" and headlights don't dim, or only dim slightly** _____.

   > **NOTE** This fault is likely an electrical fault caused by solenoid contacts or starter motor brushes that are excessively worn.

   c. **Loud repeated clicking "machine guns" when the key is turned to "crank":** _____

   > **NOTE** This fault is likely an electrical fault that may be caused by high resistance in the starter feed cable, a short circuit in the main starter feed cable after the starter relay, or the hold-in windings in the solenoid are open.

   d. **The starter engages and tries to crank, or cranks the engine slowly and the headlights went substantially dim:**

   > **NOTE** This fault could be an electrical fault or a mechanical fault. It may be caused by a discharged or weak battery, a shorted or dragging starter motor, or an engine that is mechanically bound up, such as from a hydro-locked cylinder, spun main bearing, or seized accessory drive on the engine. Turn the engine over by hand to determine if It is caused by a mechanical condition.

e. **The engine cranks substantially faster than normal:**

> **NOTE** This fault is likely a mechanical fault caused by low compression due to a broken or slipped timing belt/chain, bent valves, or piston rings that are not sealing.

3. **Diagnose the problem based on these conditions. List the steps you took to diagnose the problem and the results you obtained:**

4. **Determine any necessary actions:**

5. **Have your supervisor/instructor verify satisfactory completion of this procedure, any observations found, and any necessary action(s) recommended.**

Performance Rating

CDX Tasksheet Number: C314

0	1	2	3	4

Supervisor/instructor signature _____ Date _____

MAST 6C4

CDX Tasksheet Number: C312

1. Research the procedure and specifications for removing and installing the starter in the appropriate service information.

    a. List the specified starter mounting bolt torque: _____ ft-lb/N·m

    b. List the first step that should be performed prior to lifting the vehicle to remove the starter:

2. Remove the starter following the manufacturer's procedure.

    a. Have your supervisor/instructor verify the starter removal. Supervisor's/instructor's initials: _____

3. Inspect the gear teeth on the flywheel ring gear all the way around by turning the crankshaft by hand (ignition key "Off"). List your observations:

4. Install the starter following the manufacturer's procedures.

5. Restore the fuel system/ignition system to its proper operating condition. Start the vehicle and verify proper vehicle operation.

6. Have your supervisor/instructor verify satisfactory completion of this procedure, any observations found, and any necessary action(s) recommended.

Performance Rating

CDX Tasksheet Number: C312

0	1	2	3	4

Supervisor/instructor signature _____ Date _____

Inspect, adjust, and/or replace generator (alternator) drive belts; check pulleys and tensioners for wear; check pulley and belt alignment.

MAST
6D3

Time off_____

Time on_____

Total time_____

CDX Tasksheet Number: C317

1. Locate "inspecting, adjusting, and/or replacing generator (alternator) drive belts, pulleys, and tensioners; check pulley and belt alignment" in the appropriate service information for the vehicle you are working on.

   a. List the specified generator (alternator) drive belt tension:
   _____

   b. List the faults to look for when inspecting drive belts, pulleys, and tensioners:

   c. Describe how to check correct pulley and belt alignment:

   d. Locate the belt routing diagram or draw a picture of the current routing arrangement.

2. Install the fender covers.

3. Remove the vehicle drive belt(s).

4. Inspect the vehicle drive belts, pulleys, and tensioners for faults. List your observations for the following:

   a. Vehicle drive belt(s):

   b. Pulleys:

   c. Tensioners:

    d. Pulley/belt alignment:

5. **Have your instructor verify removal of belt(s) and faults found:**
   _____

6. **Reinstall the vehicle drive belts using the appropriate service information.**

7. **Re-tension the drive belt(s) using the appropriate service information.**

8. **Check for correct pulley, tensioner, and drive belt alignment.**

9. **Have your supervisor/instructor verify satisfactory completion of this procedure, any observations found, and any necessary action(s) recommended.**

Performance Rating

CDX Tasksheet Number: C317

0	1	2	3	4

Supervisor/instructor signature _____ Date _____

▶ **TASK** Perform charging system output test; determine needed action.

MAST
6D1

Time off_____

Time on_____

Total time_____

CDX Tasksheet Number: C315

1. Research "performing a charging system output test" in the appropriate service information for the vehicle you are working on. What is the specified charging system output? _____ amps at _____ volts at _____ rpm

2. Install the fender covers, exhaust hose(s), and wheel chocks, and set the parking brake.

3. Connect the charging system tester as outlined in the appropriate service information.

   a. Heavy red lead to the battery positive terminal
   b. Heavy black lead to the battery negative terminal
   c. Green/Black amps clamp around alternator output wire (facing the correct direction)

4. Have your supervisor/instructor verify your test procedure and connections. Supervisor's/instructor's initials: _____

5. Conduct the charging system output test. List the measured results at the maximum output: _____ amps at _____ volts at _____ engine rpm

6. Compare your results to the manufacturer's specifications. List your observations:

7. Determine any necessary action(s):

8. Have your supervisor/instructor verify satisfactory completion of this procedure, any observations found, and any necessary action(s) recommended.

Performance Rating

CDX Tasksheet Number: C315

0	1	2	3	4

Supervisor/instructor signature _____ Date _____

© 2019 Jones & Bartlett Learning, LLC, an Ascend Learning Company

Electrical/Electronic Systems **265**

MAST
6D5

Time off_____

Time on_____

CDX Tasksheet Number: C319

Total time_____

1. Research the procedure and specifications for performing the charging circuit voltage drop tests in the appropriate service information.

    a. List the maximum allowable voltage drop (generator output terminal to battery positive post): _____ volts

    b. List the maximum allowable voltage drop (generator housing to battery negative post): _____ volts

2. Install the fender covers, exhaust hose(s), and wheel chocks, and set the parking brake.

3. Connect the DMM as outlined in the appropriate service information.

    a. List the points that each voltmeter test lead should be connected to, to test the voltage drop between the output terminal of the alternator and the positive post of the battery:

    i. DMM black lead: _____

    ii. DMM red lead: _____

    b. List the points that each voltmeter test lead should be connected to, to test the voltage drop between the housing of the alternator and the negative post of the battery:

    i. DMM black lead: _____

    ii. DMM red lead: _____

4. Have your supervisor/instructor verify your test procedure and connections. Supervisor's/instructor's initials: _____

5. Conduct the charging system voltage drop test. List the measured results:

    a. Voltage drop between the alternator output terminal and battery positive post is: _____ V at: _____ A

    b. Voltage drop between the alternator housing and battery negative post is: _____ V at: _____ A

6. Compare your results to the manufacturer's specifications. List your observations:

7. Determine any necessary action(s):

8. **Have your supervisor/instructor verify satisfactory completion of this procedure, any observations found, and any necessary action(s) recommended.**

Performance Rating

CDX Tasksheet Number: C319

0	1	2	3	4

Supervisor/instructor signature _____ Date _____

Diagnose (troubleshoot) charging system for the cause
of undercharge, no-charge, and overcharge conditions.

MAST
6D2

CDX Tasksheet Number: C316

1. **Research the following specifications in the appropriate service information for the vehicle assigned.**

> **NOTE** Some charging systems use variable charging modes depending on the conditions present, such as battery temperature, driving condition, etc. Make sure you follow the manufacturer's specified testing procedures when testing these systems.

    a. **Rated output for the alternator being tested:** _____ **amps**

    b. **Regulated voltage:** _____ **volts**

    c. **How is the alternator full fielded on this vehicle?**

2. **Install the exhaust hose(s) and wheel chocks, and set the parking brake.**

3. **Connect the charging system tester as outlined in the appropriate service information.**

4. **Test the maximum current output of the alternator. List reading here:**
_____ **amps**

5. **Using the diode/stator setting or AC ripple setting, test the integrity of the diodes and stator. List the results:**

6. **Conduct the charging system regulated voltage test. Do this by measuring the maximum voltage that the charging system achieves while the engine runs at approximately 1500 rpm and waiting until the voltage doesn't rise any further. Do NOT allow the voltage to exceed 16 volts. Regulated voltage:** _____ **V**

7. **Compare your results to the manufacturer's specifications. List your observations:**

8. **Determine any necessary action(s):**

9. **Have your supervisor/instructor verify satisfactory completion of this procedure, any observations found, and any necessary action(s) recommended.**

Performance Rating

CDX Tasksheet Number: C316

0	1	2	3	4

Supervisor/instructor signature _____ Date _____

MAST
6D4

Time off_____

Time on_____

Total time_____

CDX Tasksheet Number: C318

1. Research the procedure for removing, inspecting and installing a generator (alternator) in the appropriate service information. List any precautions:

2. Disconnect battery negative terminal (consider using a memory minder while doing this task).

3. Remove the generator (alternator) as per the service information.

4. Inspect the generator (alternator) as per the service procedure. List any faults or defects found:

    a. Determine any necessary action(s):

5. Have your supervisor/instructor verify removal of generator (alternator). Supervisor's/instructor's initials: _____

6. Install the generator (alternator) as per the service information and properly tension the belt(s).

7. Start the engine to make sure everything is operating correctly. List your observations:

8. Have your supervisor/instructor verify satisfactory completion of this procedure, any observations found, and any necessary action(s) recommended.

Performance Rating

CDX Tasksheet Number: C318

0	1	2	3	4

Supervisor/instructor signature _____ Date _____

▶ **TASK** Identify system voltage and safety precautions
associated with high-intensity discharge headlights.

MAST
6E4

Time off_____

Time on_____

Total time_____

CDX Tasksheet Number: C564

1. **Using appropriate service information, identify system voltage and safety precautions associated with high-intensity discharge (HID) headlights.**

   a. **HID lamp voltage:** _____ **volts**

   b. **List the safety precautions required when working on HID system:**

2. **Have your supervisor/instructor verify satisfactory completion of this task.**

Performance Rating

CDX Tasksheet Number: C564

0	1	2	3	4

Supervisor/instructor signature _____ Date _____

MAST
6E3

Time off_____

Time on_____

Total time_____

CDX Tasksheet Number: C321

1. Research the headlamp or exterior lighting section in the appropriate service information for the vehicle you are working on.

    a. Type of headlights vehicle is equipped with: _____

    b. High-beam bulb number: _____

    c. Low-beam bulb number: _____

2. Research the headlamp aiming process in the appropriate service information for the vehicle you are working on. List (or print off and attach) the steps that are required to aim these headlamps:

> **NOTE** Do not touch the bulb with your fingers. Some bulbs will fail prematurely due to the oils from your skin.

3. Aim the headlamps following the specified procedure.

4. List any challenges you had performing this task:

5. Have your supervisor/instructor verify satisfactory completion of this procedure.

Performance Rating

CDX Tasksheet Number: C321

0	1	2	3	4

Supervisor/instructor signature _____ Date _____

Diagnose (troubleshoot) the cause of incorrect operation
of warning devices and other driver information systems;
determine needed action.

MAST
6F2

Time off_____

Time on_____

Total time_____

CDX Tasksheet Number: C325

Vehicle used for this activity:

Year _____ Make _____ Model_____

Odometer_____ VIN_____

1. **List the customer concern/complaint regarding incorrect operation of warning devices and other driver information systems:**

2. **Research the particular complaint/concern in the appropriate service information. List the possible causes:**

   a. **List any relevant specifications:**

3. **Diagnose the cause of the concern/complaint using the service information and wiring diagrams. List your tests and their results:**

4. **List the cause of the concern/complaint:**

5. **Determine any needed action(s) to correct the fault:**

6. **Have your supervisor/instructor verify satisfactory completion of this procedure, any observations found, and any needed action(s) recommended.**

Performance Rating

CDX Tasksheet Number: C325

0	1	2	3	4

Supervisor/instructor signature _____ Date _____

Inspect and test gauges and gauge sending units for cause
of abnormal gauge readings; determine needed action.

MAST
6F1

Time off_____

Time on_____

Total time_____

CDX Tasksheet Number: C646

1. List the customer concern/complaint regarding abnormal gauge readings:

2. Research the particular complaint/concern in the appropriate service
   information. List the possible causes:

   a. List any relevant gauge or sending unit specifications:

3. Diagnose the cause of the concern/complaint using the service information and
   wiring diagrams. List your tests and their results:

4. List the cause of the concern/complaint:

5. Determine any needed action(s) to correct the fault:

6. **Have your supervisor/instructor verify satisfactory completion of this procedure, any observations found, and any needed action(s) recommended.**

Performance Rating

CDX Tasksheet Number: C646

0	1	2	3	4

Supervisor/instructor signature _____ Date _____

Time off_____

Time on_____

Total time_____

CDX Tasksheet Number: C1003

1. Research the description and operation of each maintenance indicator and the procedure for resetting the maintenance indicators in the appropriate service information. List each of the maintenance indicators and the reset procedure:

2. Turn the ignition switch to the on/run position (Key On, Engine Off-KOEO). List the status of each maintenance indicator:

3. Start the engine and allow it to run for a few minutes. List the status of each maintenance indicator:

4. List any maintenance indicators that are showing required maintenance:

5. Ask your supervisor/instructor if you should carry out the reset procedure for any maintenance indicators that are showing required maintenance.

6. Have your supervisor/instructor verify satisfactory completion of this procedure, any observations found, and any necessary action(s) recommended.

Performance Rating

CDX Tasksheet Number: C1003

0	1	2	3	4

Supervisor/instructor signature _____ Date _____

Diagnose (troubleshoot) the cause of brighter-than-normal, intermittent, dim, or no-light operation; determine needed action.

MAST
6E1

Time off_____

Time on_____

Total time_____

CDX Tasksheet Number: C320

Vehicle used for this activity:

Year _____ Make _____ Model_____

Odometer_____ VIN_____

1. **List the customer complaint/concern regarding the lighting system fault:**

2. **If the lights are dim or do not operate, go to step 3. If the lights are too bright, go to step 9.**

3. **Research the affected lighting system troubleshooting section and the wiring diagram(s) in the appropriate service information for the vehicle you are working on.**

4. **Turn on the affected light(s), measure the battery voltage, and list it here: _____ volts**

5. **Measure the voltage across the power and ground at the light (light illuminated). List the voltage: _____ volts**
   a. **Calculate the total voltage drop in the circuit and list it here: _____ volt drop**
   b. **Is the voltage drop excessive? Yes: _____ No: _____**
   c. **If yes, go to step 7. If no, go to step 6.**

6. **Inspect the bulb and connections for any faults (wrong bulb, corroded, or loose connection). List your observations:**

7. **Measure the voltage drop from the battery positive post to the input terminal of the light.**
   a. **List the voltage drop: _____ volts**
   b. **Is this within specifications? Yes: _____ No: _____**
   c. **Determine any necessary action(s):**

8. Measure the voltage drop from the bulb ground to the battery negative post.

    a. List the voltage drop: _____ volts

    b. Is this within specifications? Yes: _____ No: _____

    c. Determine any necessary action(s):

9. Install exhaust hose(s) and wheel chocks, and set the parking brake. Start the vehicle.

10. Measure the charging system voltage at the battery, with the engine running at 1500 rpm: _____ volts

    a. Is this within specification? Yes: _____ No: _____

> **NOTE** If the battery voltage is too high, you will need to perform charging system checks to determine the cause of the overcharge.

11. List your observations:

12. Determine any necessary action(s):

13. Have your supervisor/instructor verify satisfactory completion of this procedure, any observations found, and any necessary action(s) recommended.

Performance Rating

CDX Tasksheet Number: C320

0	1	2	3	4

Supervisor/instructor signature _____ Date _____

Inspect interior and exterior lamps and sockets
including headlights and auxiliary lights
(fog lights/driving lights); replace as needed.

MAST
6E2

Time off_____

Time on_____

Total time_____

CDX Tasksheet Number: C956

1. Inspect the operation of the following interior lights (vehicles have different arrangements, so find as many as possible). List your observations for each light listed:

   a. Dome: _____

   b. Map: _____

   c. Dash: _____

   d. Kick panel: _____

   e. Glove box: _____

   f. Vanity mirror: _____

   g. Rear passenger: _____

   h. Other: _____

2. Inspect the operation of the following exterior lights (vehicles have different arrangements, so find as many as possible):

   a. Rear tail: _____

   b. License: _____

   c. Rear-side marker: _____

   d. Brake: _____

   e. Center high-mount stoplight: _____

   f. Back-up: _____

   g. Front park: _____

   h. Front-side marker: _____

   i. Low beam: _____

   j. High beam: _____

   k. Fog: _____

   l. Driving: _____

   m. Cornering: _____

   n. Clearance: _____

   o. Under-hood: _____

   p. Trunk: _____

   q. Other: _____

3. Ask your instructor which bulbs he/she would like you to remove. List them here:

4. List the name of the light and the bulb number for each bulb you removed:

5. Inspect/clean the sockets for each bulb you removed.

6. Ask your supervisor/instructor if you should apply dielectric grease to the socket of the bulb you have removed.

7. Reinstall the bulb into the socket and reinstall any other pieces that were removed to gain access to the bulb.

8. Have your supervisor/instructor verify satisfactory completion of this procedure.

Performance Rating

CDX Tasksheet Number: C956

| 0 | 1 | 2 | 3 | 4 |

Supervisor/instructor signature _____ Date _____

Identify safety precautions for high voltage systems on electric, hybrid, hybrid-electric, and diesel vehicles.

MAST
6B7

Time off_____

Time on_____

Total time_____

CDX Tasksheet Number: C561

1. Research the safety precautions for all high-voltage systems and methods of identifying those systems on the electric, hybrid, hybrid-electric, or diesel vehicle.

   a. List the systems that use or create high voltage:

   b. List any safety precautions when working on or around these systems and circuits:

2. Locate and point out, on the vehicle, the high-voltage circuits and components to your instructor.

3. Have your supervisor/instructor verify satisfactory completion of this procedure, any observations found, and any necessary action(s) recommended.

Performance Rating

CDX Tasksheet Number: C561

0	1	2	3	4

Supervisor/instructor signature _____ Date _____

Identify hybrid vehicle auxiliary (12V) battery service,
repair, and test procedures.

MAST
6B9

CDX Tasksheet Number: C874

1. Research the hybrid vehicle auxiliary (12V) battery service, repair, and test procedures in the appropriate service information.

    a. Does this vehicle use a 12V auxiliary battery? Yes: _____
       No: _____

    b. List any special testing, service, or repair procedures related to the 12V auxiliary battery:

2. If you performed any tests, services, or repairs on the 12V auxiliary battery, list all tests or service performed and any results:

3. Determine any necessary action(s):

4. Have your supervisor/instructor verify satisfactory completion of this procedure, any observations found, and any necessary action(s) recommended.

Performance Rating

CDX Tasksheet Number: C874

0	1	2	3	4

Supervisor/instructor signature _____ Date _____

Research vehicle service information including refrigerant/oil type, vehicle service history, service precautions, and technical service bulletins.

MAST
7A2

CDX Tasksheet Number: C342

1. Using the VIN for identification, use the appropriate source to access the vehicle's service history in relation to prior related HVAC system work or customer concerns.

   a. List any related repairs/concerns and their dates:

2. Research the HVAC system description and operation in the appropriate service information.

   a. Specified refrigerant: _____
   b. Refrigerant capacity: _____ lb/kg
   c. Specified lubricant: _____
   d. Lubricant capacity: _____ oz/mL
   e. List the specified service precautions when servicing this system:

3. Using the VIN for identification, access any relevant technical service bulletins for the particular vehicle on which you are working in relation to any related HVAC issues.

   a. List any related service bulletins and their titles:

4. Have your supervisor/instructor verify satisfactory completion of this procedure, any observations found, and any necessary action(s) recommended.

Performance Rating

CDX Tasksheet Number: C342

0	1	2	3	4

Supervisor/instructor signature _____ Date _____

Identify and interpret heating and air conditioning concern; determine needed action.

MAST
7A1

Time off_____

Time on_____

Total time_____

CDX Tasksheet Number: C341

1. List the customer's heating and air conditioning–related concern(s):

2. Research the particular concern in the appropriate service information.

   a. List the possible causes:

3. Inspect the vehicle to determine the cause of the concern.

   a. List the steps you took to determine the fault(s):

4. List the cause of the concern(s):

5. List the necessary action(s) to correct the fault(s):

6. Have your supervisor/instructor verify satisfactory completion of this procedure, any observations found, and any necessary action(s) recommended.

Performance Rating

CDX Tasksheet Number: C341

0	1	2	3	4

Supervisor/instructor signature _____ Date _____

▶ **TASK** Demonstrate use of the three Cs: concern, cause, and correction.

Additional Task

CDX Tasksheet Number: N/A

1. **Using the following scenario, write up the three Cs as listed on most repair orders. Assume that the customer authorized the recommended repairs.**

   A late model vehicle with 114,000 miles and equipped with an expansion-valve style HVAC system is brought into your shop with an A/C concern. The customer tells you that the A/C has not worked for the past several days. You perform a preliminary check and notice that the compressor clutch does not engage when moving the A/C controls to maximum cold with the A/C fan on high. Further testing shows the following:

   a. Normal static pressure in the system
   b. An open compressor clutch winding
   c. A dirty cabin air filter
   d. An excessively cracked engine serpentine belt
   e. A lightly leaking water pump seal
   f. A coolant freeze point of 20°F (−6°C)

   > **NOTE** Ask your instructor whether you should use a copy of the shop repair order or the three Cs below to record this information.

2. **Concern:**

3. **Cause:**

4. **Correction:**

5. **Other recommended service:**

6. Have your supervisor/instructor verify satisfactory completion of this procedure, any observations found, and any necessary action(s) recommended

CDX Tasksheet Number: N/A

0	1	2	3	4

Supervisor/instructor signature _____ Date _____

▶ **TASK** Performance test A/C system; identify problems.

MAST
7A.3

Time off_____

Time on_____

Total time_____

CDX Tasksheet Number: C824

1. Research the procedure and specifications for performance testing the A/C system in the appropriate service information.

    a. List or print off and attach to this sheet the steps to performance test the system:

    b. List or print off and attach to this sheet any specifications that the system should meet:

2. Following the specified procedure, carry out the performance test on the system. List the following readings:

    > NOTE Use an auxiliary fan for additional condenser airflow if conditions warrant.

    a. Engine rpm: _____

    b. Is the compressor clutch cycle time appropriate? Yes: _____ No: _____

    c. Ambient air temperature: _____ °F/°C

    d. A/C duct air temperature: _____ °F/°C

    e. Difference between ambient temp and A/C duct temp: _____ °F/°C

3. Did the A/C system pass the performance test? Yes: _____ No: _____

4. Determine any necessary action(s):

5. Have your supervisor/instructor verify satisfactory completion of this procedure, any observations found, and any necessary action(s) recommended.

Performance Rating

CDX Tasksheet Number: C824

0	1	2	3	4

Supervisor/instructor signature _____ Date _____

Identify abnormal operating noises in the A/C system; determine needed action.

CDX Tasksheet Number: C825

MAST
7A4

Vehicle used for this activity:

Year _____ Make _____ Model_____

Odometer_____ VIN_____

1. List the A/C noise-related concern:

2. **Start the vehicle and operate the A/C system to verify the noise concern. Try to determine the location of the noise. List your observation(s):**

3. **Research the possible cause(s) and testing procedures in the appropriate service information.**

   a. **List any possible cause(s):**

   b. **List or print off and attach to this sheet the steps for identifying the cause of the concern:**

4. **Following the specified procedure, identify the cause of the concern. List your test(s) and results:**

5. **List the cause(s) of the concern:**

6. Determine any necessary action(s) to correct the fault:

7. Have your supervisor/instructor verify satisfactory completion of this procedure, any observations found, and any necessary action(s) recommended.

© 2019 Jones & Bartlett Learning, LLC, an Ascend Learning Company

Performance Rating

CDX Tasksheet Number: C825

0	1	2	3	4

Supervisor/instructor signature _____ Date _____

► **TASK** Inspect for proper A/C condenser for airflow; determine needed action.

MAST 7B7

CDX Tasksheet Number: C356

Time off_____

Time on_____

Total time_____

Vehicle used for this activity:

Year _____ Make _____ Model_____

Odometer_____ VIN_____

1. **Research the procedure and specifications for inspecting the A/C condenser for proper airflow in the appropriate service information.**

    a. **List or print off and attach to this sheet any steps to perform this task:**

    b. **Specified condenser airflow:** _____ ft/min

2. **Following the specified procedure, inspect both sides of the A/C condenser for damage or blockage to the airflow. List your observation(s):**

3. **Following the specified procedure, use the anemometer to measure the condenser airflow:** _____ ft/min

4. **Determine any necessary action(s):**

5. **Have your supervisor/instructor verify your observations and recommendations and initial below. Supervisor's/instructor's initials:** _____

6. **Perform any necessary actions and list your observation(s):**

7. **Have your supervisor/instructor verify satisfactory completion of this procedure, any observations found, and any necessary action(s) recommended.**

Performance Rating

0	1	2	3	4

Supervisor/instructor signature _____ Date _____

MAST
7B10

Time off_____

Time on_____

Total time_____

CDX Tasksheet Number: C830

1. **Research the procedure for inspecting and cleaning the evaporator housing water drain in the appropriate service information.**

    a. **List or print off and attach to this sheet the steps to perform this task:**

2. **Following the specified procedure, inspect the evaporator housing water drain. List your observation(s):**

3. **Have your supervisor/instructor verify your observations. Supervisor's/instructor's initials:** _____

4. **Perform any necessary action(s) and list your observation(s):**

5. **Have your supervisor/instructor verify satisfactory completion of this procedure, any observations found, and any necessary action(s) recommended.**

Performance Rating

CDX Tasksheet Number: C830

0	1	2	3	4

Supervisor/instructor signature _____ Date _____

MAST
7D7

Time off_____

Time on_____

Total time_____

CDX Tasksheet Number: C655

Vehicle used for this activity:

Year _____ Make _____ Model_____

Odometer_____ VIN_____

1. **List the HVAC system odor-related customer concern:**

2. **Verify the concern by running the HVAC system through all operating conditions. List your observation(s):**

3. **Research the procedure to identify the odor concern in the appropriate service information.**

    a. **List the possible cause(s) of the concern:**

    b. **List, or print off and attach to this sheet, the steps to identify the source of the odor: (If no procedure is given, operate the system in each of the various functions, and see when the smell is the strongest.)**

4. **Following the specified procedure, inspect the HVAC system to identify the cause of the odor. List your steps and results:**

5. **List the cause of the concern:**

6. Determine any necessary action(s) to correct the fault:

7. Have your supervisor/instructor verify satisfactory completion of this procedure, any observations found, and any necessary action(s) recommended.

Performance Rating

CDX Tasksheet Number: C655

0	1	2	3	4

Supervisor/instructor signature _____ Date _____

Diagnose A/C system conditions that cause the protection devices (pressure, thermal, and/or control module) to interrupt system operation; determine needed action.

MAST
7B11

Time off_____

Time on_____

Total time_____

CDX Tasksheet Number: C350

1. List the A/C system protection device-related customer concern:

2. Research the possible cause(s) and testing procedures in the appropriate service information.
   a. List any possible cause(s):

   b. List or print off and attach to this sheet the steps for identifying the cause of the concern:

3. Following the specified procedure, identify the cause of the concern. List your test(s) and results:

4. List the cause of the concern:

5. Determine any necessary action(s) to correct the fault:

6. Have your supervisor/instructor verify satisfactory completion of this procedure, any observations found, and any necessary action(s) recommended.

Performance Rating

CDX Tasksheet Number: C350

0	1	2	3	4

Supervisor/instructor signature _____ Date _____

CDX Tasksheet Number: C347

Time off_____

Time on_____

Total time_____

1. Research the A/C leak detection procedure in the appropriate service information.

   a. List the leak detection method you will use:

2. Following the specified procedure, leak test the A/C system, including the evaporator, condenser, compressor, and all fittings and hoses.

   a. List your observation(s):

3. Determine any necessary action(s):

4. Have your supervisor/instructor verify satisfactory completion of this procedure, any observations found, and any necessary action(s) recommended.

Performance Rating

CDX Tasksheet Number: C347

0	1	2	3	4

Supervisor/instructor signature _____ Date _____

► TASK   Identify refrigerant type; select and connect proper gauge set/
test equipment; record temperature and pressure readings.

MAST
7A5

Time off_____

Time on_____

Total time_____

CDX Tasksheet Number: C650

1. Research the description, operation, and testing procedure for the A/C system in the appropriate service information.

   a. Specified refrigerant type: _____
   b. Specified testing RPM (engine): _____
   c. Does this vehicle require auxiliary condenser airflow for testing?
      Yes: _____ No: _____
   d. Specified high side-pressure range: _____ psi/kPa
   e. Specified low side-pressure range: _____ psi/kPa
   f. Specified air duct temperature range: _____ °F/°C

2. Following the specified procedure, identify the refrigerant type: _____

3. Obtain the proper gauge set/test equipment and connect it to the A/C system service ports.

4. Following the specified procedure, record the operating temperature and pressure readings below.

> **NOTE** Use an auxiliary fan for additional condenser airflow if conditions warrant.

   a. Engine tested at: _____ rpm
   b. High side-pressure range: _____ psi/kPa
   c. Low side-pressure range: _____ psi/kPa
   d. Ambient air temperature: _____ °F/°C
   e. A/C duct air temperature: _____ °F/°C
   f. Difference between ambient temp and A/C duct temp: _____ °F/°C

5. Does the A/C system perform according to specifications?
   Yes: _____ No: _____

6. Have your supervisor/instructor verify satisfactory completion of this procedure, any observations found, and any necessary action(s) recommended.

Performance Rating

CDX Tasksheet Number: C650

0	1	2	3	4

Supervisor/instructor signature _____ Date _____

Identify A/C system refrigerant; test for sealants; recover, evacuate, and charge A/C system; add refrigerant oil as required.

CDX Tasksheet Number: C836

1. **Research the procedure and specifications to identify A/C system refrigerant; test for sealants; recover the A/C system refrigerant in the appropriate service information.**

   a. **Specified type of refrigerant:** _____

   b. **Specified capacity of refrigerant:** _____ **lb/kg**

   c. **Specified refrigerant oil:** _____

   d. **Specified refrigerant oil capacity:** _____ **oz/mL**

   > NOTE Refrigerant oil capacity is only applicable in case of a system flush.

2. **List the method you will use to identify any sealant installed in the A/C system:**

3. **Following the specified procedure, test for sealant in the A/C system.**

   a. **Was sealant identified in the A/C system? Yes:** _____
   No: _____

   > NOTE If any sealants were identified notify your supervisor/instructor.

4. **List the method you will use to identify the type of refrigerant installed in the A/C system:**

5. **Following the specified procedure, identify the existing refrigerant in the A/C system.**

   a. **Type identified:** _____

   b. **Is this the specified refrigerant? Yes:** _____ **No:** _____

   c. **Determine any necessary action(s):**

6. **Following the specified procedure, recover the refrigerant installed in the A/C system.**

   a. **How much refrigerant was recovered from the system?**
   _____ **lb/kg**

   b. **How much oil was recovered, if any?** _____ **oz/mL**

c. Are these the specified amounts? Yes: _____ No: _____

d. Determine any necessary action(s):

7. Research the procedure and specifications for evacuating and charging the A/C system in the appropriate service information.

   a. If you are recharging the system using the high side service port, list the specified time for the low side pressure to reach specifications: _____ seconds

   > NOTE In the absence of a specified time, a good rule of thumb to remember is that the low side pressure should reach 0 psi within 7 seconds if the expansion valve or orifice tube is not restricted.

8. Following the specified procedure, evacuate the A/C system.

   a. Inches of mercury attained: _____

   b. Microns attained: _____

9. Have your supervisor/instructor verify the reading. Supervisor's/instructor's initials: _____

10. Following the specified procedure, add the refrigerant oil to the system, if needed.

    a. List the amount of oil you added to the system: _____ oz/mL

11. Following the specified procedure, charge the A/C system.

    a. List the amount of refrigerant you installed: _____ lb/kg

    b. Did the low side pressure rise within the specified time?
       Yes: _____ No: _____

12. Is equalizing the refrigerant hoses necessary? Yes: _____
    No: _____

13. Start the engine and operate the A/C system.

14. Is the system operating properly? List your observations including pressures and temperatures:

15. **Determine any necessary action(s):**

16. **Have your supervisor/instructor verify satisfactory completion of this procedure, any observations found, and any necessary action(s) recommended.**

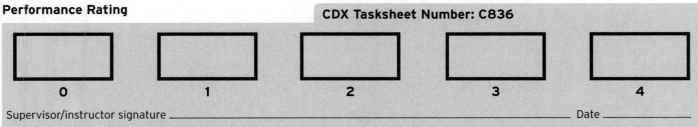

Performance Rating

CDX Tasksheet Number: C836

0	1	2	3	4

Supervisor/instructor signature _____ Date _____

CDX Tasksheet Number: C657

1. Research the procedure and specifications for this task in the appropriate service information.

   a. List the type of refrigerant you are working with: _____

   b. List the container color code for the specified refrigerant: _____

   c. What does a bottle with a yellow top and a gray bottom indicate?

   d. List or print off and attach to this sheet the steps to recycle the refrigerant:

   e. What are the labeling requirements for this refrigerant?

   f. What are the requirements for safely storing this refrigerant?

   g. Using the proper refrigerant PT (pressure/temperature) chart, record the specified reading for today's ambient temperature: _____ psi/kPa

2. Following the specified procedure, recycle the refrigerant. List your observations:

3. Following the specified procedure, ensure that the refrigerant is properly labeled. List your observations:

4. Following the specified procedure, properly store the refrigerant. List your observations:

5. Following the specified procedure, check for non-condensable gases. List your observations:

6. Have your supervisor/instructor verify satisfactory completion of this procedure, any observations found, and any necessary action(s) recommended.

Performance Rating

CDX Tasksheet Number: C657

0	1	2	3	4

Supervisor/instructor signature _____ Date _____

Inspect, remove, and/or replace A/C compressor drive belts, pulleys, and tensioners, and visually inspect A/C components for signs of leaks; determine needed action.

MAST
7B1

Time off_____

Time on_____

Total time_____

CDX Tasksheet Number: C653

1. **Research the procedure and specifications to inspect and replace drive belts, pulleys, and tensioners in the appropriate service information.**

    a. **List the specified drive belt tension:** _____ lb/kg

    b. **List the faults to look for when inspecting drive belts, pulleys, and tensioners:**

    c. **Describe how to check correct pulley and belt alignment:**

    d. **Locate the belt routing diagram, or draw a picture of the current routing arrangement below:**

2. **Following the specified procedure, remove the A/C drive belt(s).**

3. **Inspect vehicle drive belts, pulleys, and tensioners for faults. List your observations for the following components.**

    a. **Vehicle drive belt(s):**

    b. **Pulleys:**

    c. **Tensioner(s):**

    d. Pulley/belt alignment:

4. **Determine any necessary action(s):**

5. **Have your supervisor/instructor verify belt removal.**
   Supervisor's/instructor's initials: _____

> **NOTE** You may want to continue on to the next task while the belts are removed. If so, return here when you are ready to reinstall the drive belt(s).

6. **Following the specified procedure, reinstall the drive belt(s). Be sure to tension them properly.**

7. **Recheck for correct pulley, tensioner, and belt alignment. List your observation(s):**

8. **Visually inspect all A/C components for signs of leakage. List your observation(s):**

9. **Have your supervisor/instructor verify satisfactory completion of this procedure, any observations found, and any necessary action(s) recommended.**

Performance Rating

CDX Tasksheet Number: C653

0	1	2	3	4

Supervisor/instructor signature _____ Date _____

© 2019 Jones & Bartlett Learning, LLC, an Ascend Learning Company

Inspect, test, service, and/or replace A/C compressor clutch components and /or assembly; check compressor clutch air gap; adjust as needed.

MAST
7B2

Time off_____

Time on_____

Total time_____

CDX Tasksheet Number: C654

Vehicle used for this activity:

Year _____ Make _____ Model_____

Odometer_____ VIN_____

1. **Research the procedure and specifications to inspect, test, and replace the A/C compressor clutch components in the appropriate service information.**
   a. **Specified compressor clutch coil resistance:** _____ ohm
   b. **Specified compressor clutch air gap:** _____ in/mm
   c. **Specified flat rate time to replace the compressor clutch:** _____ hr

2. **Following the specified procedure, measure the resistance of the compressor clutch coil.**
   a. **Measured clutch coil resistance:** _____ ohm

3. **Following the specified procedure, measure the compressor clutch air gap.**
   a. **Measured clutch air gap:** _____ in/mm

4. **Determine any necessary action(s):**

5. **Have your supervisor/instructor verify your measurements. Supervisor's/instructor's initials:** _____

6. **If approved by your instructor, remove the A/C compressor clutch components following the specified procedure.**

7. **Have your supervisor/instructor verify removal of the clutch components. Supervisor's/instructor's initials:** _____

8. **Following the specified procedure, reinstall the A/C clutch components. Be sure that the air gap is properly adjusted. List your observation(s):**

9. Have your supervisor/instructor verify satisfactory completion of this procedure, any observations found, and any necessary action(s) recommended.

Performance Rating

0	1	2	3	4

Supervisor/instructor signature _____ Date _____

▶ TASK Remove, inspect, reinstall, and/or replace A/C compressor and mountings; determine required oil type and quantity.

MAST
7B3

Time off_____

Time on_____

Total time_____

CDX Tasksheet Number: C826

Vehicle used for this activity:

Year _____ Make _____ Model_____

Odometer_____ VIN_____

1. Research the procedure and specifications to remove, inspect, and reinstall the A/C compressor in the appropriate service information.

    a. Specified refrigerant oil type: _____

    b. Specified refrigerant oil quantity to add during replacement of the compressor: _____ oz/mL

    c. List or print off and attach to this sheet the steps to remove, inspect, and reinstall the compressor:

2. Following the specified procedure, remove the A/C compressor from the vehicle.

3. Following the specified procedure, drain the refrigerant oil from the compressor into a clean measuring container.

    a. List the quantity of oil drained: _____ oz/mL

4. Following the specified procedure, inspect the A/C compressor and mountings. List your observations:

5. Determine any necessary action(s):

6. Have your supervisor/instructor verify removal and your observations. Supervisor's/instructor's initials: _____

7. Following the specified procedure, reinstall the A/C compressor. Be sure to add the proper quantity and type of new refrigerant oil.

    a. List the quantity of oil added to the compressor: _____ oz/mL

8. Have your supervisor/instructor verify satisfactory completion of this procedure, any observations found, and any necessary action(s) recommended.

Performance Rating

CDX Tasksheet Number: C826

0	1	2	3	4

Supervisor/instructor signature _____ Date _____

MAST
7B5

CDX Tasksheet Number: C863

1. Research the conditions that require the need for an additional A/C system filter in the appropriate service information.

    a. List the conditions that require an additional filter(s):

    b. List the specified location(s) for the filter(s):

2. Following the specified procedure, inspect the system to see if an additional filter(s) is (are) needed. List your observation(s):

3. Determine any necessary action(s):

4. Have your supervisor/instructor verify your observations. Supervisor's/instructor's initials: _____

5. Following the specified procedure, install the additional filter(s), if necessary. List your observation(s):

6. Have your supervisor/instructor verify satisfactory completion of this procedure, any observations found, and any necessary action(s) recommended.

Performance Rating

CDX Tasksheet Number: C863

0	1	2	3	4

Supervisor/instructor signature _____ Date _____

Remove and inspect A/C system mufflers, hoses, lines, fittings, O-rings, seals, and service valves; perform needed action.

MAST
7B6

Time off_____

Time on_____

Total time_____

CDX Tasksheet Number: C355

Vehicle used for this activity:

Year _____ Make _____ Model_____

Odometer_____ VIN_____

1. Research the procedures and specifications for removing and inspecting the above A/C components in the appropriate service information.

   a. List or print off and attach to this sheet the procedure and specifications for inspecting these components:

2. Following the specified procedure, remove the following A/C system components. Inspect each one and list your observations below.

   a. Muffler (if equipped):

   b. Hoses and lines:

   c. Fittings, O-rings, and seals:

   d. Service valves:

3. Determine any necessary action(s):

4. Have your supervisor/instructor verify removal and observations. Supervisor's/instructor's initials: _____

5. Perform any necessary actions and list your observation(s):

6. Have your supervisor/instructor verify satisfactory completion of this procedure, any observations found, and any necessary action(s) recommended.

Performance Rating

CDX Tasksheet Number: C355

0	1	2	3	4

Supervisor/instructor signature _____ Date _____

► **TASK** Remove, inspect, reinstall, and/or replace condenser; determine required oil type and quantity.

CDX Tasksheet Number: C832

Time off_____

Time on_____

Total time_____

1. **Research the procedure and specifications for removing, inspecting, and reinstalling the condenser in the appropriate service information.**

    a. **Specified refrigerant oil type:** _____

    b. **Specified refrigerant oil quantity to add during replacement of the condenser:** _____ oz/mL

    c. **Flat rate time to R&R the condenser:** _____ hr

    d. **List, or print off and attach to this sheet, the steps to remove, inspect, and reinstall the condenser:**

2. **Before proceeding, have your instructor check your answers and obtain his or her permission to remove the condenser on this vehicle. Supervisor's/instructor's initials:** _____

3. **Following the specified procedure, remove the condenser from the vehicle.**

4. **Following the specified procedure, drain the refrigerant oil from the condenser into a clean measuring container.**

    a. **List the quantity of oil drained:** _____ oz/mL

5. **Following the specified procedure, inspect the condenser and mountings. List your observation(s):**

6. **Determine any necessary action(s):**

7. **Have your supervisor/instructor verify removal and your observations and initial below. Supervisor's/instructor's initials:** _____

8. Following the specified procedure, reinstall the condenser. Be sure to add the proper quantity and type of new refrigerant oil.

   a. List the quantity of oil added to the condenser: _____ oz/mL

9. Have your supervisor/instructor verify satisfactory completion of this procedure, any observations found, and any necessary action(s) recommended.

Performance Rating

0	1	2	3	4

Supervisor/instructor signature _____ Date _____

▶ **TASK** Remove, inspect, and reinstall receiver/drier or accumulator/drier; determine recommended oil type and quantity.

MAST
7B8

Time off_____

Time on_____

Total time_____

CDX Tasksheet Number: C829

Vehicle used for this activity:

Year _____ Make _____ Model_____

Odometer_____ VIN_____

1. Research the procedure and specifications for removing, inspecting, and reinstalling the receiver/drier or accumulator/drier in the appropriate service information.

   a. Specified refrigerant oil type: _____
   b. Specified refrigerant oil quantity to add during replacement of the receiver/drier: _____ oz/mL
   c. List or print off and attach to this sheet the steps to remove, inspect, and reinstall the receiver/drier:

2. Following the specified procedure, remove the receiver/drier or accumulator/drier from the vehicle.

3. Following the specified procedure, drain the refrigerant oil from the receiver/drier or accumulator/drier into a clean measuring container.

   a. List the quantity of oil drained: _____ oz/mL

4. Following the specified procedure, inspect the receiver/drier or accumulator/drier. List your observation(s):

5. Determine any necessary action(s):

6. Have your supervisor/instructor verify removal and your observations. Supervisor's/instructor's initials: _____

7. Following the specified procedure, reinstall the receiver/drier or accumulator/drier. Be sure to add the proper quantity and type of new refrigerant oil.

   a. List the quantity of oil added to the receiver/drier or accumulator/drier: _____ oz/mL

8. Have your supervisor/instructor verify satisfactory completion of this procedure, any observations found, and any necessary action(s) recommended.

Remove, inspect, and install expansion valve or orifice (expansion) tube.

MAST
7B9

Time off_____

Time on_____

Total time_____

CDX Tasksheet Number: C873

Vehicle used for this activity:

Year _____ Make _____ Model_____

Odometer_____ VIN_____

1. **Research the procedure and specifications for removing, inspecting, and installing the expansion valve or orifice tube in the appropriate service information.**

    a. **List any precautions for this task:**

    b. **List the specified orifice tube color or expansion valve tonnage:** _____

    c. **Does the manufacturer allow interchange of orifice colors or expansion valve tonnage? Yes:** _____ **No:** _____

    d. **List or print off and attach to this sheet the steps to perform this task:**

2. **Following the specified procedure, remove the expansion valve or orifice tube.**

    a. **List the orifice tube color or expansion valve tonnage:** _____

3. **Inspect the expansion valve or orifice tube for proper operation or debris. List your observation(s):**

4. **Determine any necessary action(s):**

5. **Have your supervisor/instructor verify removal and your observations. Supervisor's/instructor's initials:** _____

6. **Reinstall the expansion valve or orifice tube. List your observation(s):**

7. Have your supervisor/instructor verify satisfactory completion of this procedure, any observations found, and any necessary action(s) recommended.

Performance Rating

CDX Tasksheet Number: C873

0	1	2	3	4

Supervisor/instructor signature _____ Date _____

Determine procedure to remove and reinstall evaporator;
determine required oil type and quantity.

MAST
7B12

Time off_____

Time on_____

Total time_____

CDX Tasksheet Number: C831

1. **Research the procedure and specifications for removing, inspecting, and reinstalling the evaporator in the appropriate service information.**

   a. **Specified refrigerant oil type:** _____

   b. **Specified refrigerant oil quantity to add during replacement of the evaporator:** _____ oz/mL

   c. **Flat rate time to R&R the evaporator:** _____ hr

   d. **List, or print off and attach to this sheet, the steps to remove, inspect, and reinstall the evaporator:**

2. **Have your supervisor/instructor verify satisfactory completion of this procedure, any observations found, and any necessary action(s) recommended.**

Performance Rating

CDX Tasksheet Number: C831

0	1	2	3	4

Supervisor/instructor signature _____ Date _____

▶ **TASK** Inspect condition of refrigerant oil removed from the system; determine needed action.

MAST
7A7

Time off_____

Time on_____

Total time_____

CDX Tasksheet Number: C651

1. **Research the procedure for inspecting the condition of the refrigerant oil in the appropriate service information.**

    a. **List or print off and attach to this sheet the steps to inspect the refrigerant oil:**

2. **Following the specified procedure, inspect the condition of the refrigerant oil. List your observation(s):**

3. **Determine any necessary action(s):**

4. **Have your supervisor/instructor verify satisfactory completion of this procedure, any observations found, and any necessary action(s) recommended.**

Performance Rating

CDX Tasksheet Number: C651

0	1	2	3	4

Supervisor/instructor signature _____ Date _____

Determine recommended oil and oil capacity for system application.

Time off_____

Time on_____

Total time_____

CDX Tasksheet Number: C652

1. **Research the following specifications in the appropriate service information.**
   a. **Specified refrigerant oil:** _____
   b. **Specified refrigerant oil capacity:** _____ oz/mL

2. **Have your supervisor/instructor verify satisfactory completion of this procedure, any observations found, and any necessary action(s) recommended.**

Performance Rating

CDX Tasksheet Number: C652

0	1	2	3	4

Supervisor/instructor signature _____ Date _____

MAST
7E1

CDX Tasksheet Number: C656

Vehicle used for this activity:

Year _____ Make _____ Model_____

Odometer_____ VIN_____

1. **Research the operation and maintenance of the refrigerant handling equipment in the appropriate operator's manual.**

   a. **List the manufacturer of the refrigerant handling equipment:** _____

   b. **List the functions this equipment is capable of performing:**

   c. **List any required maintenance tasks and the service intervals for this equipment:**

   d. **List any special precautions when using the refrigerant handling equipment:**

   e. **Review the steps to correctly use the refrigerant handling equipment.**

   f. **List the current EPA machine standards.**

      i. **For recovery-only machines:**

      ii. **For recycling machines:**

2. Following the specified procedure, demonstrate the correct use of the refrigerant handling equipment.

   a. Recovery

      Amount of refrigerant recovered: _____ lb/kg

      Amount of oil recovered, if any: _____ oz/mL

   b. Evacuate

      Inches of mercury attained: _____

      Microns attained: _____

   c. Oil inject

      Amount of oil injected: _____ oz/mL

   d. Recharge

      Amount of refrigerant charged: _____ lb/kg

3. Determine any necessary action(s):

4. Have your supervisor/instructor verify the correct use. Supervisor's/instructor's initials: _____

5. Following the specified procedure, perform the recommended maintenance on the refrigerant handling equipment.

   a. Test the vacuum pump for proper operation.

      Inches of mercury attained: _____

      Microns attained: _____

   b. Change the vacuum oil.

      Type of oil required: _____

      Quantity of oil required: _____ oz/mL

      Condition of oil drained:

   c. Perform a leak test on the machine using specified equipment.

      Equipment used to perform this test:

      Results:

d. Change the recovery filter.

   List the filter part number: _____

e. Charge the machine with refrigerant.

   List the quantity charged: _____ lb/kg

6. Determine any necessary action(s):

7. Have your supervisor/instructor verify satisfactory completion of this procedure, any observations found, and any necessary action(s) recommended.

Performance Rating

CDX Tasksheet Number: C656

0	1	2	3	4

Supervisor/instructor signature _____ Date _____

MAST
1D11

CDX Tasksheet Number: C871

1. Research the auxiliary cooler testing procedure for this vehicle in the appropriate service information. Normally, the coolers are located either in front of the radiator or as part of the cooler end of the radiator.

   a. List the auxiliary cooler(s) this vehicle is equipped with (and the type: air-cooled, liquid cooled, etc.):

   b. List or print off and attach to this sheet the inspection and testing procedure for the cooler(s):

2. Closely examine the unit for leaks or damage that could develop into leaks under normal operating conditions. Make particular note of the condition of any tubes or hoses, and the condition of their fittings. List your test(s) and observation(s):

3. Determine any necessary action(s):

4. Return the vehicle to its beginning condition and return any tools that you may have used to their proper locations.

5. Have your supervisor/instructor verify satisfactory completion of this procedure, any observations found, and any necessary action(s) recommended.

Performance Rating

CDX Tasksheet Number: C871

0	1	2	3	4

Supervisor/instructor signature _____ Date _____

Inspect and test coolant; drain and recover coolant; flush and refill cooling system; use proper fluid type per manufacturer specification; bleed air as required.

Time off_____

Time on_____

Total time_____

CDX Tasksheet Number: C050

1. Research the following specifications/procedures for this vehicle in the appropriate service information.

    a. What is the cooling system capacity? _____ qt/lt

    b. What type of antifreeze is required? _____

    c. List or print off and attach to this sheet the cooling system bleeding procedure:

2. Coolant Test:

    a. If the vehicle is cold or cool and not running, remove the radiator cap and test the coolant's freeze protection.

        i. What is the coolant's freeze protection point? _____ °F/°C

    b. List the coolant's boiling point: _____ °F/°C at _____ psi/kPa

    c. Test the coolant's pH reading: _____

        i. Is this within specification? Yes: _____ No: _____

    d. Determine any necessary action(s):

3. Using the appropriate cooling system recycle/flush machine, flush and refill the cooling system with the correct amount of recommended antifreeze. Properly recycle/dispose of any used coolant.

    a. When this procedure is finished, retest the coolant's freeze protection: _____ °F/°C

        i. What is the coolant pH? _____

        ii. Is this within specification? Yes: _____ No: _____

    b. Follow the manufacturer's procedure to bleed air out of the cooling system, if necessary.

    c. Place exhaust hoses on the vehicle's exhaust pipe(s) and wheel chocks to prevent the vehicle from moving. Start the vehicle and monitor the cooling system to make sure that the engine warms up properly and that the thermostat opens at the correct temperature. Also, check that the coolant is at the correct level.

d. Determine any necessary action(s):

4. **Return the vehicle to its beginning condition and return any tools that you may have used to their proper locations.**

5. **Have your supervisor/instructor verify satisfactory completion of this procedure, any observations found, and any necessary action(s) recommended.**

Performance Rating

CDX Tasksheet Number: C050

0	1	2	3	4

Supervisor/instructor signature _____ Date _____

Inspect, remove, and replace water pump.

MAST
1D5

CDX Tasksheet Number: C680

1. Research the following specifications/procedures for this vehicle in the appropriate service information.

    a. Water pump bolt torque: _____ ft-lb/N·m
    b. Type of antifreeze: _____
    c. Draw or print off and attach to this sheet the belt routing diagram:

2. Drain the coolant out of the radiator. In most situations, the coolant gets replaced/recycled. If your instructor wants you to reuse the coolant, save it in a clean container and keep it free of dirt and debris.

3. Following the specified procedure, remove the water pump.

4. Inspect the pump for signs of deterioration, leaks, and worn bearings. List your observations:

5. Have your instructor verify the removal of the water pump.
   Supervisor's/instructor's initials: _____

6. Replace the water pump with a new water pump, if needed. Torque all fasteners to the proper torque.

7. Reinstall the removed coolant (or new coolant) into the radiator. Top off with the correct coolant, if needed.

8. Pressure test or vacuum test the cooling system to check for leaks. Repair any leaks found.

9. Apply the vehicle's parking brake or secure the vehicle with wheel chocks to prevent the vehicle from rolling. Also, place the exhaust hose over the exhaust pipe(s).

10. Start the vehicle and check for any leaks or overheating. Immediately shut off the vehicle if a leak or overheating is found. Repair any leaks, or determine the reason for overheating if present.

11. Return the vehicle to its beginning condition and return any tools that you may have used to their proper locations.

12. Have your supervisor/instructor verify satisfactory completion of this procedure, any observations found, and any necessary action(s) recommended.

Performance Rating

CDX Tasksheet Number: C680

0	1	2	3	4

Supervisor/instructor signature _____ Date _____

Inspect, replace, and/or adjust drive belts, tensioners, and pulleys; check pulley and belt alignment.

MAST
1D3

Time off_____

Time on_____

Total time_____

CDX Tasksheet Number: C734

1. Locate "inspecting, adjusting and or replacing a generator (alternator) drive belts, pulleys, and tensioners; check pulley and belt alignment" in the appropriate service information for the vehicle you are working on.

    a. List the specified drive belt tension: _____

    b. List the faults to look for when inspecting drive belts, pulleys, and tensioners:

    c. Describe how to check the correct pulley and belt alignment:

    d. Locate the belt routing diagram, or draw a picture of the current routing arrangement:

2. Remove the vehicle drive belt(s).

3. Inspect the vehicle drive belts, pulleys, and tensioners for faults. List your observations for the following parts:

    a. Vehicle drive belt(s):

    b. **Pulleys:**

    c. **Tensioner(s):**

    d. **Pulley/belt alignment:**

4. **Have your instructor verify the removal of the belt(s) and the faults found. Supervisor's/instructor's initials:** _____

5. **Reinstall the vehicle drive belts using the appropriate service information.**

6. **Re-tension the drive belt(s) using the appropriate service information.**

7. **Check for the correct pulley, tensioner, and drive belt alignment.**

8. **Determine any necessary action(s):**

9. **Have your supervisor/instructor verify satisfactory completion of this procedure, any observations found, and any necessary action(s) recommended.**

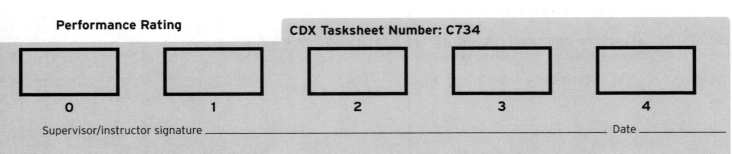

Performance Rating

CDX Tasksheet Number: C734

| 0 | 1 | 2 | 3 | 4 |

Supervisor/instructor signature _____ Date _____

▶ **TASK** Inspect engine cooling and heater system hoses and pipes; perform needed action.

MAST
7C1

Time off_____

Time on_____

Total time_____

CDX Tasksheet Number: C364

Vehicle used for this activity:

Year _____ Make _____ Model_____

Odometer_____ VIN_____

1. Research the procedure and specifications for inspecting and replacing cooling system hoses and belts in the appropriate service information.

    a. Specified change interval for radiator hoses: _____ miles/months
    b. Specified change interval for heater hoses: _____ miles/months
    c. Describe what to look for when inspecting cooling system hoses:

2. Inspect the cooling and heater system hoses. List your observations:

3. Using a cooling system pressure tester, pressurize the cooling system to the specified radiator cap pressure. Inspect the cooling system for leaks. List your observations:

4. Have your supervisor/instructor verify your observations. Supervisor's/instructor's initials: _____

5. Perform any necessary actions and list your observation(s):

6. Have your supervisor/instructor verify satisfactory completion of this procedure, any observations found, and any necessary action(s) recommended.

Performance Rating

CDX Tasksheet Number: C364

0	1	2	3	4

Supervisor/instructor signature _____ Date _____

MAST
1D7

Time off_____

Time on_____

Total time_____

CDX Tasksheet Number: C735

1. Research the thermostat replacement procedure for this vehicle in the appropriate service information.

   a. List any special procedures and/or tools to perform this task:

   b. List the thermostat housing bolt torque: _____ ft-lb/N·m

2. Look up the flat rate time for this task in a flat rate manual: _____ hr

3. Drain enough coolant out of the radiator to lower the level below the thermostat. Save this to put back in the system when the task is finished. Keep it free of dirt and debris.

4. Follow the manufacturer's procedure and remove the thermostat.

5. Carefully scrape off any old gasket residue from the thermostat housing and mating surface. Be careful not to gouge the sealing surfaces.

6. Have your instructor verify removal of the thermostat. Supervisor's/instructor's initials: _____

   NOTE Ask your supervisor/instructor whether or not to perform the next action before proceeding.

7. Test the old thermostat in a pan of boiling water to see at what temperature it opens. Suspend the thermostat in a pan of heated water using a piece of wire. The thermostat should be fully immersed in water, but do not allow it to touch the side or bottom of the pan.

   a. List the temperature at which the thermostat started to open: _____ °F/°C

   b. List the temperature at which the thermostat was fully open: _____ °F/°C

   c. How far did the thermostat open? _____ in/mm

   d. Did the thermostat operate according to specifications?
      Yes: _____ No: _____

8. Install a new thermostat and gasket/seal (or reinstall the old one if your instructor directed you to do so). Torque bolts to the proper torque.

   NOTE Be careful when bolting down the thermostat housing. Make sure the thermostat is still in its recessed groove. Failure to do so will result in a broken housing and damaged thermostat. If in doubt, ask your supervisor/instructor.

9. Once the thermostat is installed, return the drained antifreeze back into the system.

10. Follow the manufacturer's procedure to bleed any air from the cooling system.

11. Apply the vehicle's parking brake and secure the vehicle with wheel chocks to prevent the vehicle from rolling. Also, place the exhaust hose over the exhaust pipe(s).

12. Start the vehicle and check for any leaks or overheating. Immediately shut off the vehicle if a leak or overheating is found. Repair any leaks, or determine the reason for overheating if present.

13. Return the vehicle to its beginning condition and return any tools that you may have used to their proper locations.

14. Have your supervisor/instructor verify satisfactory completion of this procedure, any observations found, and any necessary action(s) recommended.

Performance Rating

CDX Tasksheet Number: C735

0	1	2	3	4

Supervisor/instructor signature _____ Date _____

CDX Tasksheet Number: C598

Vehicle used for this activity:

Year _____ Make _____ Model_____

Odometer_____ VIN_____

Time off_____

Time on_____

Total time_____

1. **List the customer concern in relation to the overheating problem:**

2. **Research the particular concern in the appropriate service information and list the possible causes:**

3. **Inspect the cooling system and engine to determine the cause of the concern. List your tests and results:**

4. **Determine any necessary action(s) to correct the fault:**

5. **Return the vehicle to its beginning condition and return any tools that you may have used to their proper locations.**

6. **Have your supervisor/instructor verify satisfactory completion of this procedure, any observations found, and any necessary action(s) recommended.**

Performance Rating

CDX Tasksheet Number: C598

0	1	2	3	4

Supervisor/instructor signature _____ Date _____

Perform cooling system pressure and dye tests to identify leaks; check coolant condition; inspect and test radiator, pressure cap, coolant recovery tank, heater core , and galley plugs; determine needed action.

CDX Tasksheet Number: C578

1. **Research the following specifications for this vehicle in the appropriate service information.**

   a. Radiator cap pressure rating: _____ psi/kPa

   b. Cooling system capacity: _____ qt/lt

   c. Type of coolant: _____

   d. Specified pH: _____

2. **Cooling System Pressure Test: If the vehicle is cold or cool, and the engine is not running, remove the radiator cap. Top off the radiator with the correct type of coolant/water mix if it is not already full. Install the proper adapter on the cooling system access point. Pressurize the cooling system to the specified radiator cap pressure listed above (or a maximum of 2 psi higher). Make sure you leave the system pressurized for a minimum of 10 minutes while you inspect for coolant leaks.**

   > **NOTE** Do not forget to check the heater core and the core plugs.

   a. **List any leaks found and any necessary action(s):**

3. **Coolant Condition: Remove the pressure tester from the radiator. Fit the proper adapter on the tester so that you can check the radiator cap.**

   a. **Pressure-test the cap and check it for the following information.**

      i. At what pressure does it vent? _____ psi/kPa

      ii. At what pressure does it hold? _____ psi/kPa

      iii. Determine any necessary action(s):

4. **Check Coolant Condition: With the engine cold or cool, and the pressure cap removed, check the condition and level of the coolant.**

   a. **Do a visual inspection of the coolant. List your findings and any necessary action(s).**

   b. **Check the level of the coolant in both the overflow bottle and the radiator. List your findings and any necessary action(s).**

5. **Radiator, Recovery Tank, and Hoses: Inspect the radiator, recovery tank, and hoses for damage or broken/missing pieces. List your findings and any necessary action(s):**

6. **Radiator Test: Reinstall the radiator cap on the radiator. Place the exhaust hose over the vehicle's exhaust pipe(s). Start the vehicle and allow the engine to warm up.**
   a. **Use the infrared temperature gun to measure the temperature across the radiator core. The temperature should show a steady cooling reading as you trace the core tubes from the hot side of the radiator to the cool side. Any tubes that are significantly cooler than the others indicate a plugged tube in the radiator.**
   b. **List your observations and determine any necessary action(s):**

7. **Have your supervisor/instructor verify satisfactory completion of this procedure, any observations found, and any necessary action(s) recommended.**

Performance Rating

CDX Tasksheet Number: C578

0	1	2	3	4

Supervisor/instructor signature _____ Date _____

© 2019 Jones & Bartlett Learning, LLC, an Ascend Learning Company

Verify engine operating temperature; determine needed action.

MAST
8A10

CDX Tasksheet Number: C398

1. Research the following specifications in the service information.

   a. Thermostat opening temperature: _____ °F/°C

   b. Temperature at which the electric fan comes on (if equipped): _____ °F/°C

   c. Temperature at which the fan clutch engages (on) (if equipped): _____ °F/°C

2. Apply the vehicle's parking brake and secure the vehicle with wheel chocks to prevent the vehicle from rolling.

3. Start the vehicle. Allow the vehicle to warm up while monitoring the engine temperature with the temp gun. Find the spot where the highest temperature reading is found on the engine side of the thermostat housing (on most engines). Monitor the temperature at that spot.

   > **NOTE** The temperature should rise to between the thermostat opening temperature and the electric (or clutch) fan "on" temperature (if equipped). If this happens, continue to the next step. If the engine doesn't get that hot, diagnose the problem and go to step 4 below. Do NOT allow the engine to overheat!

   a. If the engine is equipped with an electric fan, the temperature should vary between the electric fan "on" temperature and the electric fan "off" temperature. Record these temperatures:

   i. Electric fan "on" temp: _____ °F/°C

   ii. Electric fan "off" temp: _____ °F/°C

   b. If the engine is equipped with a clutch fan, the temperature should rise above the thermostat opening temperature but not above the clutch fan engagement temperature. Record these two temperatures:

   i. Clutch fan "engaged" temp: _____ °F/°C

   ii. Clutch fan "disengaged" temp: _____ °F/°C

   c. If the engine is equipped with a mechanical fan without a clutch, the temperature should rise to, or slightly above, the thermostat opening temperature and should remain fairly steady. Record this operating temperature:

   i. Engine operating temperature: _____ °F/°C

4. If the engine did not reach the specified thermostat opening temperature, list the max temperature reached: _____ °F/°C

5. Determine any necessary action(s):

6. Have your supervisor/instructor verify satisfactory completion of this procedure, any observations found, and any necessary action(s) recommended.

Performance Rating

CDX Tasksheet Number: C398

0	1	2	3	4

Supervisor/instructor signature _____ Date _____

▶ **TASK** Inspect and test fan(s), fan clutch (electrical or mechanical), fan shroud, and air dams determine needed action.

MAST
1D8

Time off_____

Time on_____

Total time_____

CDX Tasksheet Number: C053

Mechanical Fans:

1. Research the fan inspection and testing procedure for this vehicle in the appropriate service information.

   a. List or print off and attach to this sheet the inspection and testing procedure for the fan system:

2. Visually inspect the fan and fan clutch for damage or wear and list your observations:

3. Test the fan clutch according to the specified procedure and list your observations:

4. Determine any necessary action(s):

Electric Fans:

1. Research the fan inspection and testing procedure for this vehicle in the appropriate service information.

   a. List or print off and attach to this sheet the inspection and testing procedure for the fan system:

   b. List the temperature at which the electric fan should turn on: _____ °F/°C

2. Visually inspect the fan for damage or wear and list your observations:

3. Test the fan system according to the specified procedure and list your observations:

4. Determine any necessary action(s):

Fan Shroud and Air Dam:

1. Visually inspect the fan shroud and air dam for any damage, missing parts, or wear and list your observations:

2. Determine any necessary action(s):

3. Return the vehicle to its beginning condition and return any tools that you may have used to their proper locations.

4. Have your supervisor/instructor verify satisfactory completion of this procedure, any observations found, and any necessary action(s) recommended.

Performance Rating

CDX Tasksheet Number: CO53

0	1	2	3	4

Supervisor/instructor signature _____ Date _____

Inspect and test heater control valve(s); perform needed action.

MAST
7C2

Time off_____

Time on_____

Total time_____

CDX Tasksheet Number: C370

Vehicle used for this activity:

Year _____ Make _____ Model_____

Odometer_____ VIN_____

1. **Research the procedure and specifications for inspecting and testing the heater control valve(s) in the appropriate service information.**

   a. **Specified type of heater control valve(s): Cable: _____ Vacuum: _____ Electric: _____**

   b. **What does the temperature adjusting mechanism regulate? Coolant:_____ Air: _____**

2. **Following the specified procedure, inspect and test the heater control valve(s). List your tests and observation(s):**

3. **Determine any necessary action(s):**

4. **Have your supervisor/instructor verify satisfactory completion of this procedure, any observations found, and any necessary action(s) recommended.**

Performance Rating

CDX Tasksheet Number: C370

0	1	2	3	4

Supervisor/instructor signature _____ Date _____

MAST
1D6

CDX Tasksheet Number: C052

1. Research the following specifications/procedures for this vehicle in the appropriate service information.

    a. Cooling system capacity: _____ qt/lt
    b. Type of antifreeze: _____

2. Drain as much coolant from the vehicle as possible into a clean drain pan so that you can reuse the coolant. Also, place the drain pan so that dirt and other debris will not contaminate it while removing the radiator.

3. Follow the specified procedure to remove the radiator.

> **NOTE** Be careful when removing the hoses from the radiator. You will need to slide a thin tool (such as a small screwdriver) carefully between the hose and the radiator fitting to loosen the hose, or slit the hose and carefully peel it off of the fitting. Failure to do this could cause damage to the radiator fitting.

4. Inspect the radiator for any damage and list your observation(s):

5. Have your instructor verify the removal of the radiator.
   Supervisor's/instructor's initials: _____

6. Reinstall the radiator following the specified procedure.

7. Reinstall the removed coolant into the radiator. Top off with the correct coolant, if needed.

8. Pressure test or vacuum test the cooling system to check for leaks. Repair any leaks found.

9. Apply the vehicle's parking brake or secure the vehicle with wheel chocks to prevent the vehicle from rolling. Also, place the exhaust hose over the exhaust pipe(s).

10. Start the vehicle and check for any leaks or overheating. Immediately shut off the vehicle if a leak or overheating is found. Repair any leaks, or determine the reason for overheating if present.

11. Have your supervisor/instructor verify satisfactory completion of this procedure, any observations found, and any necessary action(s) recommended.

Performance Rating

CDX Tasksheet Number: C052

0	1	2	3	4

Supervisor/instructor signature _____ Date _____

Determine procedure to remove, inspect, reinstall, and/or replace heater core.

Time off_____

Time on_____

Total time_____

CDX Tasksheet Number: C864

Vehicle used for this activity:

Year _____ Make _____ Model_____

Odometer_____ VIN_____

1. **Research the procedure and specifications for inspecting and replacing the heater core in the appropriate service information.**

    a. **List the flat rate time for removing and replacing the heater core:**
       _____ hr

    b. **Does this task require evacuation of the A/C refrigerant?**
       Yes _____ No _____

    c. **List, or print off and attach to this sheet, the steps to remove and replace the heater core:**

2. **List, or print off and attach to this sheet, the steps to inspect the heater core:**

3. **Have your supervisor/instructor verify satisfactory completion of this procedure, any observations found, and any necessary action(s) recommended.**

Performance Rating

CDX Tasksheet Number: C864

0	1	2	3	4

Supervisor/instructor signature _____ Date _____

▶ **TASK** Identify hybrid vehicle A/C system electrical circuits
and the service/safety precautions.

MAST
7B4

CDX Tasksheet Number: C827

Vehicle used for this activity:

Year _____ Make _____ Model_____

Odometer_____ VIN_____

1. **Research the description and operation of a hybrid vehicle A/C system in the appropriate service information.**

    a. **What powers the A/C compressor (prime mover)?**

    b. **Does the manufacturer use a special designation for the A/C system electrical circuits? Yes: _____ No: _____**
       i. **If yes, what is it?**

    c. **List the voltage(s) that the A/C system electrical circuits operate on:**

    d. **How is the A/C compressor driven? V belt: _____ Serpentine belt: _____ Direct drive: _____ Other (specify below)**
       i. **Specified refrigerant: _____**

       ii. **Refrigerant capacity: _____ lb/kg**

       iii. **Specified lubricant: _____**

       iv. **Lubricant capacity: _____ oz/mL**

       v. **List the specified safety precautions when servicing this system:**

2. Have your supervisor/instructor verify satisfactory completion of this procedure, any observations found, and any necessary action(s) recommended.

Performance Rating

CDX Tasksheet Number: C827

0	1	2	3	4

Supervisor/instructor signature _____ Date _____

Check operation of automatic or semi-automatic
HVAC control systems; determine needed action.

MAST
7D8

Time off_____

Time on_____

Total time_____

CDX Tasksheet Number: C866

Vehicle used for this activity:

Year _____ Make _____ Model_____

Odometer_____ VIN_____

1. **Research the description and operation of the HVAC climate control system in the appropriate service information.**

   a. **Is this system a full-authority climate control system? Yes: _____**
   No: _____

   b. **If equipped, how do you test the evaporator thermistors?**

   c. **If equipped, how do you test the three-wire A/C pressure sensors?**

   d. **If equipped, how do you access the trouble codes on this vehicle?**

   e. **How is the heater controlled? Heater control valve: _____ Blend door: _____**

   f. **Research the steps to test the operation of the climate control system:**

2. **Following the specified procedure, test the operation of the climate control system. List your steps and the results:**

3. **Determine any necessary action(s):**

4. **Have your supervisor/instructor verify satisfactory completion of this procedure, any observations found, and any necessary action(s) recommended.**

Performance Rating

CDX Tasksheet Number: C866

0	1	2	3	4

Supervisor/instructor signature _____ Date _____

CDX Tasksheet Number: C566

Time off_____

Time on_____

Total time_____

Vehicle used for this activity:

Year _____ Make _____ Model_____

Odometer_____ VIN_____

1. **List the HVAC-related customer concern:**

2. **Start the vehicle and operate the HVAC system to verify the concern. List your observation(s):**

3. **Following the specified procedure, connect a scan tool to the vehicle. Obtain and record the following information.**

   a. **HVAC-related trouble code(s) and their description(s):**

   b. **HVAC-related data (list at least three readings and their descriptions):**

4. **Have your supervisor/instructor verify satisfactory completion of this procedure, any observations found, and any necessary action(s) recommended.**

Performance Rating

CDX Tasksheet Number: C566

0	1	2	3	4

Supervisor/instructor signature _____ Date _____

Inspect and test HVAC system control panel assembly; determine needed action.

MAST
7D4

Time off_____

Time on_____

Total time_____

CDX Tasksheet Number: C376

Vehicle used for this activity:

Year _____ Make _____ Model_____

Odometer_____ VIN_____

1. List the A/C-heater control panel–related HVAC customer concern:

2. Verify the concern by operating each of the control panel controls through their range and list your observation(s):

3. Research the procedure and specifications for inspecting and testing the A/C-heater control panel in the appropriate service information.

   a. What kind of controls is this vehicle equipped with? _____
   b. List or print off and attach to this sheet the steps to inspect and test the control panel:

4. Following the specified procedure, inspect and test the control panel. List your tests and results:

5. List the cause of the concern:

6. Determine any necessary action(s) to correct the fault:

7. Have your supervisor/instructor verify satisfactory completion of this procedure, any observations found, and any necessary action(s) recommended.

Performance Rating

CDX Tasksheet Number: C376

0	1	2	3	4

Supervisor/instructor signature _____ Date _____

Inspect and test HVAC system control cables, motors, and linkages; perform needed action.

Time off_____

Time on_____

Total time_____

CDX Tasksheet Number: C865

Vehicle used for this activity:

Year _____ Make _____ Model_____

Odometer_____ VIN_____

1. **Research the procedures and specifications to inspect and test the control cables, motors, and linkages in the appropriate service information.**

    a. **List any precautions for this task:**

    b. **List or print off and attach to this sheet any procedures and specifications for this task:**

2. **Verify the operation of all HVAC control cables, motors, and linkages. List your observation(s):**

3. **Following the specified procedure, inspect and test the cables, motors, and linkages. List your tests and results:**

4. **Determine any necessary action(s):**

5. **Have your supervisor/instructor verify satisfactory completion of this procedure, any observations found, and any necessary action(s) recommended.**

Performance Rating

CDX Tasksheet Number: C865

0	1	2	3	4

Supervisor/instructor signature _____ Date _____

▶ TASK Diagnose temperature control problems in the HVAC system; determine needed action.

CDX Tasksheet Number: C362

Time off_____

Time on_____

Total time_____

1. List the heater/ventilation-related customer concern:

2. Research the customer concern in the appropriate service information. List the possible causes:

3. Following the specified procedure, diagnose the customer concern. List your tests and observations:

4. List the cause of the customer concern:

5. Determine any necessary action(s) to correct the fault:

6. Have your supervisor/instructor verify satisfactory completion of this procedure, any observations found, and any necessary action(s) recommended.

Performance Rating

CDX Tasksheet Number: C362

0	1	2	3	4

Supervisor/instructor signature _____ Date _____

© 2019 Jones & Bartlett Learning, LLC, an Ascend Learning Company

HVAC and Electrical Accessories **381**

▶ TASK Inspect HVAC system ducts, doors, hoses, cabin filters, and outlets; perform needed action.

MAST
7D6

Time off_____

Time on_____

Total time_____

CDX Tasksheet Number: C378

Vehicle used for this activity:

Year _____ Make _____ Model_____

Odometer_____ VIN_____

1. **Research the procedure and specifications for inspecting the above components in the appropriate service information.**

    a. **Is this vehicle equipped with a cabin air filter? Yes:** _____
    No: _____

    b. **What is the recommended replacement interval for the cabin air filter?**
    _____ **mi/km/mo**

2. **Following the specified procedure, inspect the following components. List your observations below.**

    a. **Ducts:**

    b. **Doors:**

    c. **Hoses:**

    d. **Cabin filter(s):**

    e. **Outlets:**

3. **Determine any necessary action(s):**

4. **Have your supervisor/instructor verify satisfactory completion of this procedure, any observations found, and any necessary action(s) recommended.**

Performance Rating

CDX Tasksheet Number: C378

0	1	2	3	4

Supervisor/instructor signature _____ Date _____

Inspect and test HVAC system blower, motors, resistors, switches, relays, wiring, and protection devices; determine needed action.

MAST
7D1

Time off_____

Time on_____

Total time_____

CDX Tasksheet Number: C373

Vehicle used for this activity:

Year _____ Make _____ Model_____

Odometer_____ VIN_____

1. **Research the procedure and specifications to inspect and test the electrical components of the HVAC system in the appropriate service information.**

   a. Specified resistance of the blower motor: _____ ohms

   b. Specified resistance of the blower motor resistors

   Resistance on the highest resisted speed: _____ ohms

   Resistance on medium-high resisted speed: _____ ohms

   Resistance on medium-low resisted speed: _____ ohms

   Resistance on the lowest resisted speed: _____ ohms

   c. **List all the protection devices for the blower motor circuit:**

2. **Following the specified procedure, inspect and test the following devices. List your observations below.**

   a. **Blower motor:**

   b. **Blower motor resistors:**

   c. **Appropriate switches:**

   d. **Appropriate relays:**

e. Appropriate circuit protection devices:

f. Appropriate wiring harness:

3. Determine any necessary action(s):

4. Have your supervisor/instructor verify satisfactory completion of this procedure, any observations found, and any necessary action(s) recommended.

Performance Rating

CDX Tasksheet Number: C373

0	1	2	3	4

Supervisor/instructor signature _____ Date _____

► **TASK** Diagnose A/C compressor clutch control systems; determine needed action.

MAST 7D2

Time off_____

Time on_____

Total time_____

CDX Tasksheet Number: C374

Vehicle used for this activity:

Year _____ Make _____ Model_____

Odometer_____ VIN_____

1. **Research the procedure and specifications to inspect and test the electrical components of the A/C compressor clutch control system in the appropriate service information.**

    a. Specified resistance of the clutch winding: _____ ohms

    b. A/C cycling switch specifications (if equipped)
       Off pressure: _____ psi/kPa
       On pressure: _____ psi/kPa

    c. A/C thermoswitch specifications (if equipped)
       Off temperature: _____ °F/°C
       On temperature: _____ °F/°C

    d. A/C duct temperature specifications: _____ °F/°C

    e. A/C high-pressure cut-out switch specifications
       Off pressure: _____ psi/kPa
       On pressure: _____ psi/kPa

    f. A/C low pressure cut-out switch (non-cycling) (if equipped)
       Off pressure: _____ psi/kPa
       On pressure: _____ psi/kPa

    g. A/C compressor clutch relay specifications (if equipped)
       Relay winding resistance: _____ ohms
       Maximum allowable voltage drop across relay contacts:
       _____ volts

    h. List all the fuses and/or fusible links for the A/C compressor clutch circuit:

    i. Does the compressor clutch share a fuse with the blower circuit?
       Yes: _____ No: _____

2. **Following the specified procedure, activate the A/C system.**

    a. Does the compressor clutch engage? Yes: _____ No: _____
    b. If yes, continue on to step 3. If no, skip to step 5.

3. **List your observations below.**

    a. A/C cycling switch readings (if equipped)
       Off pressure: _____ psi/kPa
       On pressure: _____ psi/kPa

    b. A/C thermoswitch readings (if equipped)
       Off temperature: _____ °F/°C
       On temperature: _____ °F/°C

    c. A/C duct temperature: _____ °F/°C

    d. **A/C high pressure cut-out switch readings (may require condenser airflow blockage to test). (DUE TO THE SAFETY IMPLICATIONS, ONLY PERFORM THIS TEST IF APPROVED BY YOUR SUPERVISOR/INSTRUCTOR.)**
       Off pressure: _____ **psi/kPa**
       On pressure: _____ **psi/kPa**
    e. **Determine any necessary action(s):**

4. **Have your supervisor/instructor verify the readings. Supervisor's/instructor's initials:** _____

> **NOTE** If your instructor signed off on this step, skip to the final check off.

5. **If the clutch does not engage, install a gauge set and check for minimum refrigerant pressure. If pressure is insufficient, check for refrigerant leaks, then retest after repair. If pressure is sufficient, measure the voltage applied to the compressor clutch winding.**

    a. **Applied voltage to the compressor clutch:** _____ **volts**
    b. **Compressor clutch winding resistance:** _____ **ohms**
    c. **A/C compressor clutch relay readings**
       Relay winding resistance: _____ **ohms**
       Voltage at the relay contact input terminal: _____ **volts**
       Voltage drop across relay contacts (A/C on): _____ **volts**
    d. **Describe the circuit protection device(s) condition:**

6. **Determine any necessary action(s):**

> **NOTE** If repairs are made, return to step 3 and retest.

7. **Have your supervisor/instructor verify satisfactory completion of this procedure, any observations found, and any necessary action(s) recommended.**

Performance Rating

CDX Tasksheet Number: C374

0	1	2	3	4

Supervisor/instructor signature _____ Date _____

© 2019 Jones & Bartlett Learning, LLC, an Ascend Learning Company

Diagnose malfunctions in the vacuum, mechanical, and electrical components and controls of the heating, ventilation, and A/C (HVAC) system; determine needed action.

MAST
7D3

Time off_____

Time on_____

Total time_____

CDX Tasksheet Number: C835

Vehicle used for this activity:

Year _____ Make _____ Model_____

Odometer_____ VIN_____

1. List the vacuum, mechanical, or electrical controls–related HVAC customer concern:

2. Verify the concern by operating each of the HVAC vacuum, mechanical, and electrical controls through their range and list your observation(s):

3. Research the procedure, specifications, and wiring diagrams for diagnosing the concern in the appropriate service information.

    a. List the possible faults:

    b. List or print off and attach to this sheet the steps to diagnose the fault:

4. Following the specified procedure, diagnose the concern. List your tests and the results:

5. List the cause of the concern:

6. Determine any necessary action(s) to correct the fault:

7. Have your supervisor/instructor verify satisfactory completion of this procedure, any observations found, and any necessary action(s) recommended.

Performance Rating

☐ 0   ☐ 1   ☐ 2   ☐ 3   ☐ 4

Supervisor/instructor signature _____ Date _____

▶ TASK Diagnose operation of comfort and convenience accessories and related circuits (such as: power window, power seats, pedal height, power locks, trunk locks, remote start, moon roof, sun roof, sun shade, remote keyless entry, voice activation, steering wheel controls, back-up camera, park assist, cruise control, and auto dimming headlamps); determine needed repairs.

MAST
6G1

Time off_____

Time on_____

Total time_____

CDX Tasksheet Number: C330

1. **Ask your instructor to assign a vehicle with a fault in a comfort and convenience accessory circuit. List the circuit:**

2. **List the customer concern/complaint:**

3. **Locate the diagnosis section and the wiring diagram for the comfort and convenience accessory fault in the appropriate service information for the vehicle you are working on. Briefly describe the diagnostic procedure for this vehicle's comfort and convenience accessory circuit (or attach diagnosis printout):**

4. **Following the specified procedure, diagnose faults in the comfort and convenience accessory circuit. List your tests and their results:**

5. **List the cause of the customer concern/complaint:**

6. **Determine any needed repair(s) to correct the fault:**

7. **Have your supervisor/instructor verify satisfactory completion of this procedure, any observations found, and any needed repair(s) recommended.**

Performance Rating

CDX Tasksheet Number: C330

0	1	2	3	4

Supervisor/instructor signature _____ Date _____

► TASK Diagnose operation of security/anti-theft systems and related circuits (such as: theft deterrent, door locks, remote keyless entry, remote start, and starter/fuel disable); determine needed repairs.

MAST
6G2

CDX Tasksheet Number: C340

Vehicle used for this activity:

Year _____ Make _____ Model_____

Odometer_____ VIN_____

1. **Locate the diagnostic procedure for the security/anti-theft system in the appropriate service information for the vehicle you are working on.**

   a. **List the safety precautions to be taken when working on the security/anti-theft system:**

   b. **List the diagnostic procedures for the security/anti-theft system (or print and attach copy):**

2. **Check for any DTCs in the security/anti-theft system. List the DTCs and their descriptions here:**

3. **Following the specified procedure, diagnose faults in the security/anti-theft system. List your tests and observations:**

4. **Determine any needed repair(s) to correct the fault:**

5. Have your supervisor/instructor verify satisfactory completion of this procedure, any observations found, and any needed repair(s) recommended.

Performance Rating

CDX Tasksheet Number: C340

0	1	2	3	4

Supervisor/instructor signature _____ Date _____

Diagnose operation of entertainment and related circuits (such as: radio, DVD, remote CD changer, navigation, amplifiers, speakers, antennas, and voice-activated accessories); determine needed repairs.

MAST
6G3

Time off_____

Time on_____

Total time_____

CDX Tasksheet Number: C336

Vehicle used for this activity:

Year _____ Make _____ Model_____

Odometer_____ VIN_____

1. **Ask your instructor to assign a vehicle with a fault in the radio or entertainment system.**

2. **List the customer concern/complaint:**

3. **Locate the diagnostic procedure for the related customer concern/complaint in the appropriate service information for the vehicle you are working on. Briefly describe the diagnostic procedure for the fault (or attach diagnosis printout):**

4. **Following the specified procedure, diagnose the related customer concern/ complaint. List your tests and their results:**

5. **List the cause of the customer concern/complaint:**

6. **Determine any needed repair(s) to correct the customer concern/complaint:**

7. Have your supervisor/instructor verify satisfactory completion of this procedure, any observations found, and any needed repair(s) recommended.

Performance Rating

CDX Tasksheet Number: C336

0	1	2	3	4

Supervisor/instructor signature _____ Date _____

► **TASK** Diagnose operation of safety systems and related circuits (such as: horn, airbags, seat belt pretensioners, occupancy classification, wipers, washers, speed control/collision avoidance, heads-up display, park assist, and back-up camera); determine needed repairs.

MAST
6G4

CDX Tasksheet Number: C327

1. **Ask your instructor to assign a vehicle/simulator with a fault in a safety system. List the system:**

2. **List the customer concern/complaint:**

3. **Locate the diagnosis section and the wiring diagram for the safety system fault in the appropriate service information for the vehicle you are working on. Briefly describe the diagnostic procedure for this vehicle's safety system (or attach diagnosis printout):**

4. **Following the specified procedure, diagnose faults in the safety system. List your tests and their results:**

5. **List the cause of the customer concern/complaint:**

6. **Determine any needed repair(s) to correct the fault:**

7. Have your supervisor/instructor verify satisfactory completion of this procedure, any observations found, and any needed repair(s) recommended.

Performance Rating

CDX Tasksheet Number: C327

0	1	2	3	4

Supervisor/instructor signature _____ Date _____

Diagnose body electronic system circuits using a scan tool; check for module communication errors (data communication bus systems); determine needed action.

MAST
6G5

Time off_____

Time on_____

Total time_____

CDX Tasksheet Number: C338

1. Locate "diagnosis of body electronic systems with a scan tool" in the appropriate service information for the vehicle you are working on.

    a. List the safety precautions to be taken when working on the body electronic systems:

    b. List the diagnostic procedures for the body electronic systems (or print and attach copy):

2. Check for any DTCs (diagnostic trouble codes) in the BCM (body control module) and list them and their descriptions here:

3. Following the specified procedure, diagnose faults in the body electronic system. List your tests and observations:

4. Determine any needed action(s) to correct the fault:

5. Have your supervisor/instructor verify satisfactory completion of this procedure, any observations found, and any needed action(s) recommended.

Performance Rating

CDX Tasksheet Number: C338

0	1	2	3	4

Supervisor/instructor signature _____ Date _____

CDX Tasksheet Number: C649

Vehicle used for this activity:

Year _____ Make _____ Model_____

Odometer_____ VIN_____

1. **List the customer concern(s) related to software updates or the need for reprogramming electronic modules:**

2. **Verify the concern and list your observations including any codes, their descriptions, or any TSBs:**

3. **Research the correct method to perform software transfers, software updates, or reprogramming on electronic modules in appropriate service information.**

   a. **List any precautions here:**

   b. **List the steps needed to reprogram the electronic module (or print and attach):**

   c. **Have your instructor verify your process:** _____

4. Have your supervisor/instructor verify satisfactory completion of this procedure, any observations found, and any necessary action(s) recommended.

Performance Rating

CDX Tasksheet Number: C649

0	1	2	3	4

Supervisor/instructor signature _____ Date _____

Diagnose operation of entertainment and related circuits (such as: radio, DVD, remote CD changer, navigation, amplifiers, speakers, antennas, and voice-activated accessories); determine needed repairs.

MAST
6G3

Time off_____

Time on_____

Total time_____

CDX Tasksheet Number: C336

Vehicle used for this activity:

Year _____ Make _____ Model_____

Odometer_____ VIN_____

1. **Ask your instructor to assign a vehicle with a fault in the radio or entertainment system.**

2. **List the customer concern/complaint:**

3. **Locate the diagnostic procedure for the related customer concern/complaint in the appropriate service information for the vehicle you are working on. Briefly describe the diagnostic procedure for the fault (or attach diagnosis printout):**

4. **Following the specified procedure, diagnose the related customer concern/ complaint. List your tests and their results:**

5. **List the cause of the customer concern/complaint:**

6. **Determine any needed repair(s) to correct the customer concern/complaint:**

7. Have your supervisor/instructor verify satisfactory completion of this procedure, any observations found, and any needed repair(s) recommended.

Performance Rating

CDX Tasksheet Number: C336

0	1	2	3	4

Supervisor/instructor signature _____ Date _____

Appendix: CDX/NATEF Correlation Guide

Section IN 102: Driving Your Performance

CDX Tasksheet Number	2017 MAST NATEF Reference and Priority	Corresponding Page(s)
C451	OA1; P-1	1-2
C460	OA9; P-1	3
C456	OA6; P-1	5
C458	OA7; P-1	7-8
C459	OA8; P-1	9
C465	OA15; P-1	11
NN00	N/A	13
C461	OA10; P-1	15
C462	OA11; P-1	17
C463	OA12; P-1	19
C455	OA5; P-1	21
NN	N/A	23
C472	OC1; P-1	25
C590	OC5; P-1	27
C475	OC4; P-1	29
C474	OC3; P-1	31
C468	OB3; P-1	33
C452	OA2; P-1	35
C467	OB2; P-1	37-39
C466	OB1; P-1	41-44
C896	OB5; P-1	45
C469	OB4; P-1	47
C819	6B5; P-1	49-50
C820	6B6; P-1	51
C886	1A7; P-1	53-54
C473	OC2; P-1	55

CDX Tasksheet Number	2017 MAST NATEF Reference number and Priority	Corresponding Page(s)
C453	0A3; P-1	57
C454	0A4; P-1	59-60
C476	0D1; P-1	61-62
C737	1D10; P-1	63-64
C239	5B9; P-1	65
C177	4B9; P-1	67
C902	2A4; P-1	69
C734	1D3; P-1	71-72
C962	8D5; P-1	73
C898	1A3; P-1	75
C464	0A13; P-1	77-78
C895	0A14; P-1	79

Section AT 101: Engine Repair

CDX Tasksheet Number	2017 MAST NATEF Reference and Priority	Corresponding Page(s)
C885	1A1; P-1	81
C002	1A2; P-1	83-84
C900	1A9; P-2	85
NN01	N/A	87-88
NN09	N/A	89
C392	8A5; P-1	91
C393	8A6; P-2	93-94
C709	8A7; P-1	95-96
C395	8A8; P-1	97
C390	8A3; P-3	99-100
C004	1A4; P-1	101-102
C671	1A10; P-3	103-105
C679	1C1; P-1	107
C029	1C2; P-1	109-110
C030	1C3; P-2	111-112
C727	1C5; P-2	113
C728	1C7; P-1	115-116
C036	1C8; P-2	117
C729	1C9; P-3	119
C733	1D13; P-2	121
C726	1C4; P-2	123
C678	1C10; P-2	125-126
C730	1C13; P-2	127-128

CDX Tasksheet Number	2017 MAST NATEF Reference number and Priority	Corresponding Page(s)
C034	1C6; P-3	129-130
C597	1C11; P-2	131
C040	1C12; P-2	133-134
C731	1C14; P-1	135-136
C723	1B4; P-1	137
C541	1A5; P-1	139-140
C596	1A8; P-2	141-142
C899	1A6; P-1	143-144
C676	1B5; P-1	145-146
C677	1B6; P-1	147
C675	1B8; P-3	149-150
C673	1B1; P-1	151-152
C674	1B2; P-1	153
C720	1B10; P-3	155-156
C719	1B9; P-3	157
C718	1B7; P-3	159-160
C721	1B11; P-3	161-162
C021	1B3; P-2	163
C722	1B12; P-2	165
C724	1B13; P-3	167-168
C027	1B14; P-3	169-170
C737	1D10; P-1	171-172
C1003	6F3; P-2	173-174
C732	1D9; P-1	175-176
C736	1D12; P-2	177-178
C871	1D11; P-3	179
C050	1D4; P-1	181-182
C680	1D5; P-2	183-184
C734	1D3; P-1	185-186
N/A	N/A	187-188
C364	7C1; P-1	189
C735	1D7; P-1	191-192
C598	1D2; P-1	193
C578	1D1; P-1	195-196
C398	8A10; P-1	197-198
C053	1D8; P-1	199-200
C370	7C2; P-2	201
C052	1D6; P-2	203-204
C864	7C4; P-2	205

Section AT 103: Electrical/Electronic Systems

CDX Tasksheet Number	2017 MAST NATEF Reference and Priority	Corresponding Page(s)
C286	6A1; P-1	207
C296	6A4; P-1	209-210
C951	6A2; P-1	211-212
NN06	N/A	213-214
C952	6A7; P-1	215-216
C299	6A10; P-1	217-218
C955	6A12; P-1	219
C641	6A3; P-1	221
C291	6A5; P-1	223-224
C295	6A6; P-1	225-226
C298	6A9; P-1	227-228
C313	6C5; P-2	229-230
C642	6A11; P-2	231-232
C819	6B5; P-1	233-234
C820	6B6; P-1	235
C644	6B4; P-1	237-238
C302	6B1; P-1	239-240
C818	6B2; P-1	241-242
C645	6B8; P-1	243
C304	6B3; P-1	245-246
C817	6A8; P-1	247-248
NN12	N/A	249-250
C1002	6C7; P-2	251
C309	6C1; P-1	253-254
C310	6C2; P-1	255
C311	6C3; P-2	257
C314	6C6; P-2	259-260
C312	6C4; P-1	261
C317	6D3; P-1	263-264
C315	6D1; P-1	265
C319	6D5; P-1	267-268
C316	6D2; P-1	269-270
C318	6D4; P-1	271
C564	6E4; P-2	273
C321	6E3; P-2	275
C325	6F2; P-2	277-278

CDX Taksheet Number	2017 MAST NATEF Reference and Priority	Corresponding Page(s)
C646	6F1; P-2	279-280
C1003	6F3; P-2	281-282
C320	6E1; P-1	283-284
C956	6E2; P-1	285-286
C561	6B7; P-2	287
C874	6B9; P-2	289

Section AT 208: HVAC and Electrical Accessories

CDX Taksheet Number	2017 MAST NATEF Reference and Priority	Corresponding Page(s)
C342	7A2; P-1	291
C341	7A1; P-1	293
NN07	N/A	295-296
C824	7A3; P-1	297
C825	7A4; P-2	299-300
C356	7B7; P-1	301-302
C830	7B10; P-1	303
C655	7D7; P-2	305-306
C350	7B11; P-2	307
C347	7A6; P-1	309
C650	7A5; P-1	311
C836	7E2; P-1	313-315
C657	7E3; P-1	317-318
C653	7B1; P-1	319-320
C654	7B2; P-2	321-322
C826	7B3; P-2	323-324
C863	7B5; P-3	325
C355	7B6; P-2	327-328
C832	7B13; P-2	329-330
C829	7B8; P-2	331-332
C873	7B9; P-1	333-334
C831	7B12; P-2	335
C651	7A7; P-2	337
C652	7A8; P-1	339
C656	7E1; P-1	341-343
C871	1D11; P-3	345
C050	1D4; P-1	347-348
C680	1D5; P-2	349-350
C734	1D3; P-1	351-352

CDX Tasksheet Number	2017 MAST NATEF Reference and Priority	Corresponding Page(s)
C364	7C1; P-1	353
C735	1D7; P-1	355–356
C598	1D2; P-1	357
C578	1D1; P-1	359–360
C398	8A10; P-1	361–362
C053	1D8; P-1	363–364
C370	7C2; P-2	365
C052	1D6; P-2	367–368
C864	7C4; P-2	369
C827	7B4; P-2	371–372
C866	7D8; P-2	373
C566	7A9; P-3	375
C376	7D4; P-3	377
C865	7D5; P-3	379
C362	7C3; P-2	381
C378	7D6; P-1	383
C373	7D1; P-1	385–386
C374	7D2; P-2	387–388
C835	7D3; P-2	389
C330	6G1; P-2	391–392
C340	6G2; P-2	393–394
C336	6G3; P-3	395–396
C327	6G4; P-1	397–398
C338	6G5; P-2	399
C649	6G6; P-2	401–402
C336	6G3; P-3	403–404